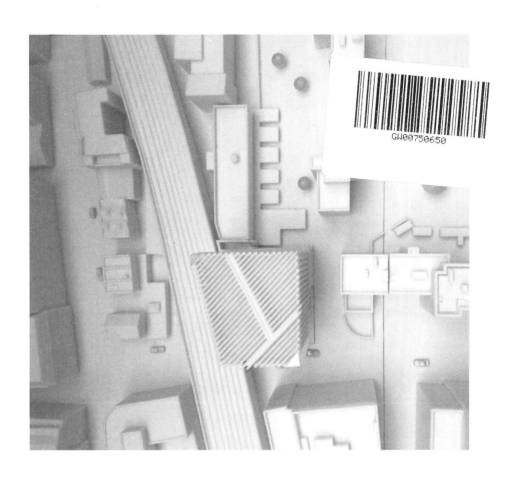

DIGITAL CRAFT

3D PRINTING FOR ARCHITECTURAL DESIGN BRYAN RATZLAFF

Published in the United Kingdom in 2016 by
Lee 3D Ltd
35a Walnut Tree Walk
London SE11 6DN
Telephone: +44 (0) 207 582 3904

Enquiries and orders: www.lee3d.co.uk/digitalcraft

ISBN 978-0-9935087-0-7

Design by Bryan Ratzlaff
Printed in the United Kingdom

DIGITAL CRAFT

3D PRINTING FOR ARCHITECTURAL DESIGN BRYAN RATZLAFF

Published by Lee 3D

CONTENTS

PREFACE

The formation of this book was a long time in the making, even if I had not realised it at the time. Five years ago, after completing my undergrad in Canada, I was on my way to London to look for work experience. Although I had other reasons to be in London, my timing could not have been worse for my architectural career, as the Great Recession still had its grips on the industry. However, I soon found myself working for architects in a previously unimagined capacity: as a 3D printing specialist, learning about the technology and its potential and creating models for architects and designers with my newly developed expertise.

After gaining this valuable experience, I returned to university to complete my masters degree in architecture. While studying, I took up a further position in 3D printing for architects, and it was during this time that de-powdering a particular model triggered a line of thought that gradually led to this piece of research. The model had been designed by Steffian Bradley Architects and used a combination of subtle colour, geometric abstraction and cleverly edited details that made me question the banality of much of the other work I had seen. It was made obvious to me in an instant that there was more potential in 3D printing architectural models than most architects might be exploring. This thought stayed with me throughout my final year of studies, and through a shared curiosity in this matter with George Lee, this book project was launched as soon as I graduated.

Digital Craft is both a critical analysis of the models use in the design process and an exploration of the effect that 3D printing has on its use and creation. Contributing to the digital skillset of architects and designers, the book also explores some of the techniques that can be applied to a 3D printed architectural model, which can aid the representation of information, space and ideas. The book lays out a collection of ideas that designers can build upon and create their own catalogue of stylistic techniques for creating intelligent 3D printed models.

In reading this book, it is hoped that both those already using the technology and those new to it can gain a better understanding of the 3D printed model as an object of digital craft. Although 3D printing may be perceived as a complex process, there is no reason for a model not to reach its full potential from a lack of design engagement. Architects need not concern themselves with all the technicalities of 3D printing, but an understanding of the capabilities of the technology and the extent of what can be accomplished can increase a model's value as a design and communication tool.

ACKNOWLEDGEMENTS

Many thanks are due to those who have helped this research materialise into a book.

I would first and foremost like to thank George and Christabelle Lee for providing me with the opportunity to make this project happen. This experience allowed me to develop an idea on 3D printing in architecture into a justified position, and having their experience was both instrumental and enjoyable in coming to this conclusion.

I would also like to express my gratitude to the following people who graciously made time to be interviewed and provided input into my research: Neil Merryweather at PLP Architecture, Paul Treacy at Steffian Bradley Architects, Yui Law at Bogle Architects, Adam Nathaniel Furman at Saturated Space, Peter Murray at New London Architecture, Professor Nick Dunn at Lancaster University and Richard Beckett at the Bartlett, University College London.

Thanks are also due to those that directly provided or helped to arrange photographs for this book: Paul Treacy at Steffian Bradley Architects, SPPARC Architecture, Yui Law at Bogle Architects, Neil Merryweather at PLP Architecture, Foster + Partners, Vertex Modelling, Henning Larsen Architects, Make Architects, Zaha Hadid Architects, Jonathan Rowley at Digits2Widgets, Plowman Craven, Agnese Sanvito, Ryan Kingsnorth, and Tiemen Schotsaert at fabriek.org.

Finally, I would like to thank Isabella for routinely helping to make sense of my thoughts and for living through many evenings and weekends where my time was dedicated to *Digital Craft*.

INTRODUCTION

The contemporary architect has access to a range of representational mediums to develop and communicate their ideas. These include long established manual methods such as a sketch, and a range of digital techniques that are under constant evolution. Arguably, of all these available resources, the model is one of the most capable for visualising a design and communicating with others. Despite its recognised significance, very little research has been done on the subject, particularly compared to that on the architectural drawing and more recently, various digital means of architectural representation.

If little has been written about the architectural model, even less has been written on the 3D printed model. It is a highly relevant, yet underexplored tool in today's architectural practice. Most speculative consideration on 3D printing has thus far been of an inclusive nature, attempting to cover at once, its potential to affect a wide range of industries. Contemporary research on the architectural model may include a single chapter on 3D printing at best, and is thus limited to a general overview of the technology. Owing to this, much of what has been written on 3D printing has really only scratched the surface about its use and potential, particularly when considering a specific field such as architecture. As the technology's use continues to grow and become more affordable, it is fitting to establish a more widespread understanding of creating models with 3D printing.

Admittedly, such is the complexity of the various digital mediums accessible to an architect, that research and literature on any digital subject matter tends to concentrate on the techniques of using them – they take on a how-to approach. Likewise, this research may explore digital modelmaking techniques, but just as importantly, it critically investigates the impact of 3D printing on the architectural model. Although this may appear an obvious concept, it is worth understanding the peculiarities of the process in order to provide a platform of knowledge on which the application of digital techniques can be based upon.

3D printing has been used for nearly twenty years, yet its novelty has not worn off as it continues to develop. Therefore, it is still a relevant topic. While the technology's application as a construction method is an exciting potential, its use for modelmaking continues to grow and be accepted by an increasing amount of architects. For both those adopting the technology and those already using it, it is important to understand the shift it creates in the design process, beyond the output being made by a machine and in a different material. In doing so, they will be enabled to better exploit the 3D printing technology, ultimately increasing their model's value as a design and communication tool.

The first part of this research explores the concept of the architectural model, particularly its use within the design process and as a communication tool. It also looks at the traditional techniques of making and the impact that an applied style has on a model's identity. It sets out to identify the model's fabrication as a recognised work of craftsmanship.

Part Two analyses the effect that 3D printing has had on the architectural model, both physically and in its use. The workflow of producing a 3D printed model is compared to other model mediums, establishing that the tools and techniques used to stylise the former are in fact the architect's domain.

Part Three covers some of the possible digital techniques that can be applied to a 3D printed model, which can aid the representation of information, space and ideas. The content of this section is by no means definitive, but sets out to be a collection of ideas that designers can build upon and create their own catalogue of stylistic techniques for creating their own 3D printed models.

Although 3D printing may be perceived as a complex process, there is no reason for a model to suffer due to an architect's lack of engagement. Architects need not concern themselves with all the technicalities of 3D printing. Understanding the potentials of the technology and the extent of what can be accomplished is more important than understanding the technology itself. Up to now, this has not been greatly considered. This research explores some potential techniques that can be deployed, to make the application of personal touches and style relevant to the use of 3D printing. The theoretical framework and exploration of style and craft in modelmaking and their relevance to 3D printing are used as platform for the execution of the techniques illustrated in this book.

PART 1

THE ARCHITECTURAL MODEL

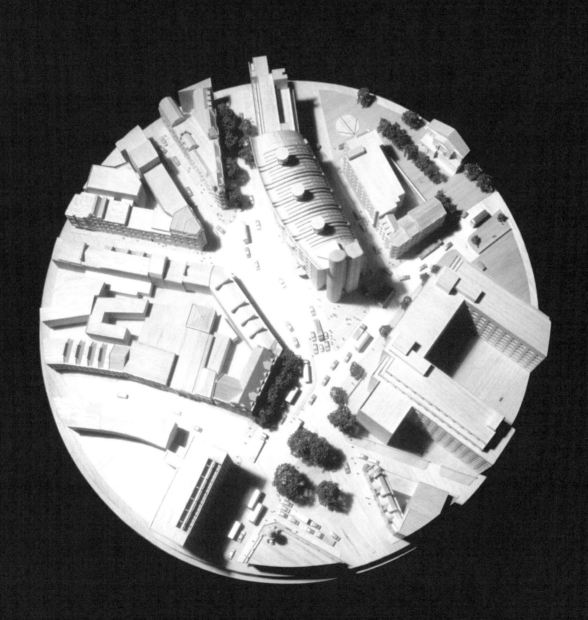

THE ARCHITECTURAL MODEL

The model has long held an important position within the realm of architectural representation, being one of the primary instruments that architects have used to communicate their designs. Of the varying modes of representation – drawings, models, photography, film, text or even an architectural object itself – the drawing and the model are the two most familiar with architects and students, used to explore ideas and communicate design decisions. But whereas the drawing can require the viewer's interpretation in order to make meaning beyond obvious comprehension, the model provides a rather simpler approach and thus a simpler existence.

At the most basic level, a model is a physical device, which translates an architect's design into a scaled object that can aid communication and understanding. It is a miniature of a building, used for experimentation, validation and conveying design intentions. It is also a craft in its own right. When used for experimentation, the process of creating a scaled model can guide solutions for spatial inefficiencies, which could otherwise not be revealed in the two-dimensional phase of a design process. When used strictly as a tool for validation, the model can be limited by predetermined decisions regarding geometry. In this instance, a model is perhaps less efficient than a drawing, which is very flexible in what it can achieve as mode of representation.

Yet the drawing by nature is abstract; its technical aspects typically consist of a measured representation of architecture, showing features as they would never be experienced by the human eye. Although these are easily drawn, they can be more difficult to comprehend. The orthographic, perspective and axonometric drawings never show a fully accurate description of the formal composition of a design. One could argue that the perspective might be the closest to achieve such accuracy, however, by showing a specific view, it limits (perhaps intentionally) the experience of space to a single source. This can also be said of a digital visualisation, essentially a screen grab of a viewport within modelling software. Also fly-through videos, which are experiencing an increase in popularity as a visualisation tool, are inherently restrictive in showing formal relationships. As a moving render, they also undergo a similar process of view selection to that of the digital visualisation.

Conversely, a model can be used to view nearly any aspect of a particular building design. The viewer has the control to change his/her viewpoint and thus direct their analysis at will. In this sense, the model is an effective tool used by the architect to better visualise the composition of space, the interaction between forms and the environment proposed by the design. It not only allows a physical validation of thoughts and drawings, but also enables a discussion to materialise and unify the various strands of the design process into a single medium, one that can be handled and observed in a range of different ways. This 'simple' usability and convergence of information are arguably the primary reason that architects make models.

The architectural model is essential in evaluating design decisions that will not come to fruition until the final product is built at full scale. Except for where empirical results are required – such as new building technologies or structural systems – architecture is generally not a design discipline that allows full-scale prototyping. The design of spatial qualities, formal composition and content arrangement are in constant evolution through the design process of a building, therefore making the task of creating a full-scale prototype an unrealistic endeavour. To replace the full-scale prototyping, the architect requires a scaled representation of the various subjective design elements.

This chapter intends to explore the nature of the model and its relationship to the architect, with particular attention to the model's use as an integral part of the design process. Moreover, it will cover the process of creating architectural models and the relating fabrication techniques, with the purpose of giving context to the wider investigation of style in digital model making. It is necessary to establish this understanding in order to analyse the changes that digital model making has created for the architectural model.

Left The model as a communication tool with the architect and the client. Denys Lasdun with Sir Laurence Olivier with the model of the Royal National Theatre, 1967.

Opposite The model as a design tool. Frank Gehry in his studio, an architect well known for designing through the use of models, 1997.

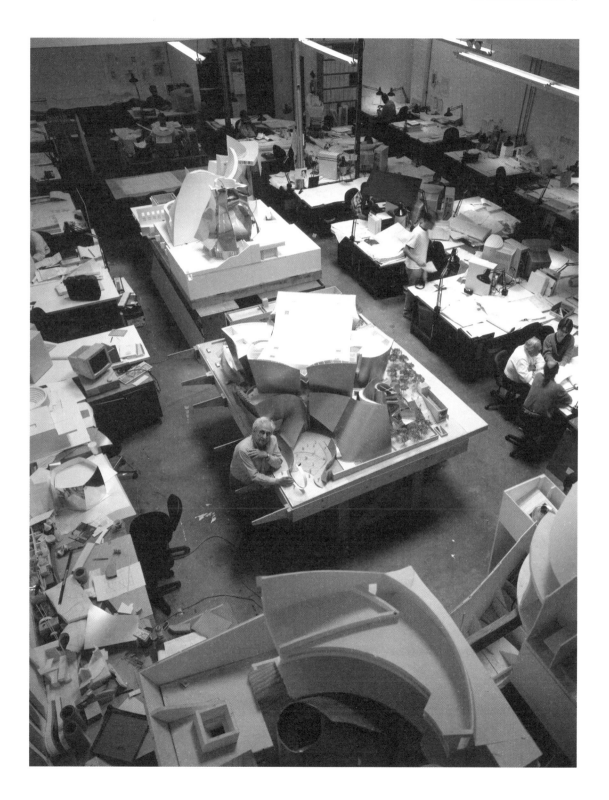

1.1 THE MODEL & THE DESIGN PROCESS

Although the practice of representing architecture in miniature form has been done for centuries, the extent to which models have been used as a medium for architects has in fact fluctuated. Contemporary architects are familiar with using models of varying purpose, style and construction in their practices. However, prior to this present streak of considerable continuity – within which, much style and material development has indeed occurred – the architectural model has gone through changing phases of prevalence and obsolescence. For instance, the beginning of the Renaissance period saw a surge of model use, while later in the sixteenth century architects relied on two-dimensional forms of representation. Models were once again more favourably utilised during the Baroque period, however both late 18th century neo-classical and Victorian architects developed a penchant for the drawing; the former preferring the elevation and perspective to display their visionary designs of grand scales, while the latter became more formally trained in drawing with precise measurements and annotation.[1]

Many developments over the 20th century enabled the models' use to increase once more and become commonplace. Firstly, as drawing has become increasingly illustrative, the model became an ideal tool for expressing the logic of a project. Also, the arrival of new architectural forms – from early Modernist movements such as Expressionism and International, to the later styles of Deconstructivism and Neo-futurism – required an extensive use of three-dimensional visualisation. In addition, the model began to be recognised as an important medium when viewed as an object of craft, primarily propagated by Peter Eisenman's 1976 exhibition Idea as Model at the New York Institute for Architecture and Urban Studies (IAUS). Finally, the modernisation of tools and materials for modelmaking has had a significant influence on the development of the model, much like 3D printing has done in the 21st century.

Although an understanding of the changing popularity of the model provides a useful contextualisation, it is more interesting for this research to explore how the model's relationship with the process of designing architecture has developed. For much of the classical era, the model was typically an instrument that would be better described as a template, often illustrating full-scale elements such as column capitals and other ornate features of classical architecture. Skilled craftsmen would use this master form to copy and create the details in a building's construction. Come the middle ages, the model's function within the design process evolved into a tool used for predicting construction methods, material use, and cost estimation.[2] These were most often carved or made of wood and depicted an entire building or façade. The use of a model for this purpose was largely born out of the fact that architectural drawing, and particularly the ability to accurately create measured drawings was underdeveloped at this time.[3] One could argue that expressing a building in three-dimensional miniature form was a more natural means of understanding a building design than a plan or an elevation, a quality, in fact, which has not dissipated over time.

Throughout the 20th century, the relationship between the architect and the model has evolved to the extent that the model and the sketchbook can go hand-in-hand during the design process. And much like the sketch, the architect's use of the model has evolved from static template to a somewhat temporary exercise. A model is primarily used to validate design solutions and may quickly become obsolete as further revisions occur. Even models used for competition entries represent a project at a stage that will likely face revisions.[4] As projects progress towards completion, models from each previous stage in the design begin to face a loss of

value for both architect and client. Often, final models of a project will then not only represent the most polished form of representation to the completed design, but will also be the most polished model amongst all others produced throughout the process. It is interesting to note however, that despite piles of unwanted models and an array of obsolete and forgotten objects, architects still possess a romantic affiliation with making models and designing in three dimensions with physical materials and tools. Karen Moon, in Modelling Messages, suggests that this 'tactile and physical contact inherent in modelmaking' gives architects a sense of gratification not found elsewhere in the design process[5].

Considering the importance of the model during the design process, it is reasonable to suggest that the greatest purpose of models is to allow architects to test, confirm, discuss and consider design solutions, in addition to common assumption that they are primarily tools for communicating ideas to others. They act in a similar manner to sketches, hand drawings, diagrams and visualisations that an architect uses for the exploration of ideas. Often, the work that is publicised by an architectural firm, whether at the end of a project or for competition purposes, rarely showcases this

Below Models made for interrogating design solutions tend to lose their value as that design has been superseded. Discarded models of the Royal National Theatre in Lasdun's model studio, 1970.

development work. Rather, they will use final drawings and models that are likely to have been reworked and refined over and over again, and possess a type of graphic standard considered suitable for representing the practice's external image. The day-to-day working drawings, sketches and models on the other hand are often unpublicised, being kept within the realms of the practice. Interestingly, they are the ones passed around the office the most and so provide the bulk of what an architect produces visually.

Amongst the few general classifications of models, this research aims to discuss the design model in particular. Design models can be broadly divided into two types: the actual process model, which comprises part of the design approach, and the study model, which in turn is used to analyse and test previous design decisions. Contemporary use of 3D printing for the most part falls into the latter category of design models, whereas the process model, also described as a sketch model, is often made by hand, with primitive materials and tools. Although aesthetically crude, this can lead to immediate design decisions and is a literal form of three-dimensional sketching and experimentation. According to Moon, these 'embryonic objects' are better able to express the architect's initial ideas and inspirational concepts of a project than the more refined drawings or models of subsequent stages. The sketch model's form can be considered as the 'purest' representation of a design's essence.[6]

The study model on the other hand, while still considered a design tool, is used for the validation of design decisions taken previously in other mediums: a sketch, drawing, computer file or even an earlier process model. The study model's use can be seen as a snapshot of a project's design progress, taken at a moment where a three-dimensional analysis is required before advancing with revision. At the same time, study models are not limited to analysis of formal design, also being used to analyse a number of other aspects, such as materiality, program use, content organisation, site context, construction details, climatic studies, and can even exist to simply facilitate discussion with stakeholders during the design process. One could suggest that the study model is utilitarian, and perhaps the most exposed to the obsolescent and disposable nature of architectural models.

At the final end of the spectrum there are models that do not participate in the design process at all. These are presentation models and can include sales and promotional models, final clients' models and other models used at the end of the project. In contrast to the models used during the design process, these final examples possess qualities that are less abstract and hence more realistic. In doing so they lack the expressive and personal characteristics of the working models, revealing less of the path taken to the development of the design.

Opposite Above Process models for the Leventis Art Gallery, by Feilden Clegg Bradley Studios. Many of the models shown possess a sketch quality, quickly created with foam, likely with an input of thought towards the design of the building.

Opposite Below Presentation models are usually made once a design is finalised and will attempt a true representation of the proposal. International competition entry for the Busan Opera House, by Henning Larsen Architects.

Due to its three-dimensional qualities, the model possesses the ability to communicate ideas that other representational medium in architecture struggle to achieve. As a result, it is an effective tool for communication between the architect and those not trained in architectural visualisation, such as clients, investors, planners and other laypeople. Whether a sketch, process or a final 'sales' model, they are able to communicate the formal intentions of a design, explain design decisions in three-dimensions, and describe contextual limitations, materiality, and so on. For instance, sketch models are more likely used to convey initial ideas between colleagues within a studio environment, since their crude features can require an architecturally trained mind to be fully understood. A study model on the other hand is more elaborate and thus better apt to impart either a set of information or a particular design consideration, which can then be used to further communicate with clients, planning authorities and other stakeholders. Finally, a model used in competition or planning processes requires a set of highly refined features in order to communicate the essence of a project to a committee as clearly and explicitly as possible.

Besides their three-dimensional qualities, models are also more effective communication tools because they are arguably more approachable and understood by a wider range of people. They are more readily com-

Opposite Models have visual, spatial and tactile appeal. KREOD pavillion model for the London 2012 Olympics (above) and design iteration models for the China International Trade Pavillion, Rio 2016 (below).

Below Models are an approachable architectural medium and are thus very engaging for a wider range of people.

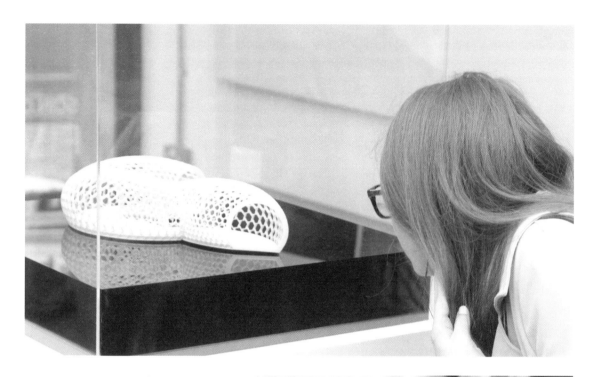

prehended than computer images, require less training to read than an architect's drawings, and can provide information about any aspect of a building. As previously discussed, most drawings require some form of interpretation; renderings are restrictive in what they can show (although this can be to their advantage); and diagrams can either be too schematic or over simplified. With the exception of some drawings, these mediums by their very nature end up being exceptionally specific in what they are able to communicate. Models on the other hand, provide the dissemination of a multitude of information in a single mode of representation. They may also be, and often are, very specific in what they convey, but even then the three-dimensionality allows the communication of the idea at hand to formulate much more effectively, due to the wealth of tangible content present.

Clients or customers in any field are rarely trained in what they are purchasing. A client in architecture, for example, may know they what they want in a building/structure, but may know little about how to read the architectural plans and drawings, or how to translate the information presented to them into an imagined vision of their building. More often than not, their building is only fully perceived once it is built. Therefore, the use of models is of utmost importance, since it provides an effective means to communicate architecture in an approachable manner. Not only are the features of the building, such as architectural proportions and materiality easier to understand, but also the physicality of the object offers the client an ability to visualise their own experience of the building. Similar to a doll's house, the scaled representation offers its viewer the ability to create and imagine stories around a building that does not exist yet.

It is the physicality of the model – its presence – that makes it such a useful communication tool, so much so that a photograph of a model will change the ways in which it is experienced and perceived. In person, the model acts as a tangible device for communicating a set of ideas, however, as a photograph it becomes a static depiction of a specific narrative. An architect can utilise photographs of a model in two ways: either as a recording method or to concentrate the viewer on a specific theme within the model, the latter of which being more common. Record images typically show the model in its entire extent, sitting on a neutral background – the model is seen as an object in its own right. These can be used for marketing purposes, such as to promote the practice's or modelmaker's technical skills as this type of photograph focuses on the material qualities of the model. It can also frame specific elements that describe more about the object's construction than the intent of the architectural design. Record images can also be used as evidence of work or as archival material. The second purpose of photographing a model may be to create a narrative.

Opposite Above Close-up photographs of a model can produce the effect of creating a narrative. Showing the spatial qualities of the project itself, this technique removes the viewers impression of the model as an object and can effectively communicate design intentions.

Opposite Below The same model as above, but now clearly showing the extents of the model. Photographed in this way, the model remains an object in the eye of the viewer.

Peter Murray, Chairman of New London Architecture (NLA), notes that 'to a certain extent, photographs of good quality hand-made models can be photographed where people use them instead of spending their money on renderings.'[7] Used in this way, the photograph acts a viewpoint, purposely restricting the viewer to a particular narrative within the model. The image is used to show intentions of the architectural design, rather than the model as an object.

Undoubtedly, there are advantages in using a pictorial representation of a model, but even then, they stress the value of the model as a physical medium; in its actual state, the model can communicate a multitude of architectural information, without the need to concentrate the viewer on a specific quality.

The physical tangibility of the model not only lends itself to approachability like no other architectural medium, but also to its ability to retain value in memory. Today, technology is consistently present in our lives and is increasingly being used to communicate architectural ideas. Recent developments of note are digital fly-throughs, animations and virtual reality. While these technologies offer very interesting platforms for architects to represent their work, the nature of their digital medium provides its own set of challenges. People consume so much content on screens and in digital formats nowadays, that it becomes ever more difficult to spark their interest for longer periods of time. The virtual environment has shortened people's attention spans, influencing how they read images and engage with what is presented to them. Moreover, the abundance of images readily available creates a state of apathy and inertia, as they start to merge into one single blur of architectural content in the minds of the

viewer. In this sense, a video by Bjarke Ingels explaining his new project and showing architectural animations becomes very routine and thus less engaging. For someone trained in architecture, the content of the video may be enough to heighten their interest to the point of engagement, but for the layperson, the medium itself might impair the content's ability to be memorable.

In contrast, the model, which may appear a dated medium, still resonates with the majority of people. Good examples are models on display for the public in places such as museums, galleries, and exhibition spaces. At The Building Centre in London, the NLA in collaboration with Pipers modelmakers, have on permanent display a 12.5m long 1:2000 model of London. Recently updated in 2015, it represents the central area of greater London and displays the upcoming developments in the city. Murray notes how the physical model engages with people in a way that other mediums are unable to, saying 'you can see with the model here, people will come and spend ages and have to be dragged away from it. They spend all their time looking at it. I think there is clearly a sort of Lilliputian element to it that probably being small and somehow it gives us feeling that we are in control of the world. The sort of fascination with dolls houses and things like that continues into adulthood and we feel somehow that the world is a less frightening place when it's a bit smaller like that. But also, I think that it is just a very good way of being able to take in the large number of variables that you have when you're looking at a map, a plan or a drawing.'[8]

Further elaborating on this point, Neil Merryweather, Head of Modelmaking and Senior Associate Partner at PLP Architecture, suggests that 'there is something that has been proven time and time again, that even the most savvy and sophisticated architecturally educated people will gather around a model on a table and ignore all of the expensively printed boards with visualisations. There is something about the way you stand a model, you look at it from your own perspective and you make the choices how you want to look at it. If you're looking at a perspective, it's a one-dimensional single point of view, and I think the model gives the viewer the impression of control. No matter how crude it is, or how abstract it is – it can be monochrome – they will bring the visualisations in their minds to the model. The human brain is fantastic like that. I think the model even as a monochrome model still speaks to people; so 3D printing is just another way of providing that.'[9]

1.2 THE MODEL & TECHNIQUES OF MAKING

Perhaps the greatest developments undergone by models throughout time have been the techniques and materials used to construct them. The resulting styles produced by different availability of technologies, materials and expertise have had a pronounced impact on the visual characteristics of models over time. One could argue that identifying a model's period of origin could be as easily done by examining its construction, as it would be by the style of architecture it represents.

Formal training of architects in modelmaking began in the early 20th century, when its recognition as an important part of the design process was increasing. Today, architecture students are expected to produce a variety of models in many different levels of skill throughout their academic training. It is at this early stage that architects learn the nuances of designing in three-dimensional mediums and using the model as an exploratory tool. In the professional environment, a number of architects still involve themselves in these initial explorations of sketch modelling. The sketch model, whether it is made with card and glue or Styrofoam, enables the architect to work with his hands and become physically engaged with the creative process. This combination of three-dimensional experimentation with sketching will form the conceptual basis that is to be translated into Computer-aided design (CAD) programs.

While the contemporary sketch model may be the domain of the architect, the requirement for more complex and polished models in architecture gave rise to the professional field of modelmaking. Modelmakers possess the ability to visualise in three-dimensions, a sense of scale, attention to detail and an ability to interpret information. The need for dedicated modelmakers increased as the model entered its renaissance in the 20th century, when they became ever more active in architectural practice. Today, most large practices employ dedicated modelmaking professionals and on top of this, there are numerous businesses dedicated to modelmaking available to architects.

The role of the modelmaker and their relationship with the architect can vary between practices. Their purpose goes beyond the actual process of making models, and they are facilitators in the exploration and communication of ideas disseminated by the model. Their skills in representing architectural concepts allows them to advise architects on how best to approach the model to maximise its potential. They can be important advisers in the design process, even at very early sketch model stages, when they are able to assist the architect with materials and technique. For instance, within Foster + Partners, there are two distinctive in-house modelmaking studios: one responsible for guiding architects through the craft of their sketch models, and the other where professional modelmakers create the more polished models used in later stages of a design.

One could suggest that the modelmaker operates as an editor of information – drawings supplied by architects can contain far more information than is required to build a model. Modelmakers need to be able to read these drawings and take out the relevant features in order to build the model. While this ability to interpret drawings, combined with the need to effectively communicate with the architect constitute important skills to the profession, their primary proficiency lies in the command of their craftsmanship. The materials, tools, and technologies used in modelmaking have developed greatly over time. Models have been made from primitive materials such as wood and cardboard and engineered sheets of acrylic and Styrofoam. A modelmaker's tool kit has gone from strictly hand held items to include a workshop worth of machinery. Most recently, there has been a surge of digital tools available for modelmaking, such as laser cutters and 3D printers. Although dismissed at first, as most new technologies are when introduced, modelmakers have now grasped these digital tools and utilised them as part of their skillset, enabling an improvement in the accuracy of models.

These developments have undoubtedly had an effect on the appearance of models. Much like the buildings they represent, models are susceptible to changes in style influenced by technology, material availability and cultural tastes in a determinant period. Within the lexicon of architectural representation, style can be identified as a unified or continuous technique within a developing body of work. A style is created by a technique applied to a particular medium, used to produce a mode of representation. It is worth noting that, although the changes in tools and techniques can influence the style of a product, they cannot do so without the skills and vision of the person that operates them. In this sense, the maker becomes the most important element in the creation of style, whose personal intentions will direct the ways in which techniques are used to manifest their design. Within architectural representation for example, a digitally produced architectural rendering can have a number of different styles depending on how the artist utilises the tools available in a particular computer software.

Artists, photographers, designers and architects utilise style to enable a body of work to be identifiable, cohesive and communicative. This personal application of style occurs also within the realm of modelmaking and independent of the technique or materials used, style can be subjectively – or even unconsciously – curated into the model. Inevitably, models are imbued with its makers' creative choices, and so are able to

Opposite Models are often used to examine a design proposal in its context. In this model, the level of detail has been applied selectively where needed. Economist Building, 25 St James's Street by Alison and Peter Smithson. 1965

convey messages about the designers themselves: about their architectural identities and approach. Similarly to a drawing, models can translate the aspects that the architect wants to project, and by doing so they are able to display how the architect wants to be seen.

While the development of a trademark style of architecture may be perceived as the greatest indicator of its creator's identity, the style of architectural representation can also be used to express who the architect is. This was especially true in an era of handmade drawings, but even digital drawings of today possess marks of their creators – a diagram by Bjarke Ingles, a render by Luxigon or a 3D printed model by Foster + Partners can all arguably be identified by their stylistic qualities, rather than the architecture they represent.

It is important to highlight that the development of a personal style can lag behind the development of the technology that makes it possible. That is to say, the mass adoption and full exploitation of a technology might take longer to be realised, even if the technology itself has been introduced for a while. The development and implementation of a style is therefore not only affected by the tools available, but can also be constrained or motivated by a user's understanding of these tools, the period's zeitgeist and changes in tastes. This is particularly evident in modelmaking in the mid to late twentieth century, when technologies remained relatively consistent, but styles developed and varied greatly.

At the root of the potential for stylising models is the inescapable balance of realism in architectural representation. In the attempt to achieve their freedom of expression in model design, architects and modelmakers abstract architectural information that could otherwise be shown as realistically as possible. Prior to the 20th century, models operated in a similar manner to drawings, attempting to depict the intended design in an accurate and realistic manner. But the development of architectural representation thereafter has been a response to the architect's desire to express the meaning or intelligence behind their design decisions. This argument was best illustrated by Michael Graves in his essay Thought Models, where he noted that models were not supposed to represent real buildings any more, but rather the ideas behind them.[10] This position has brought about a progressive reinterpretation of the model's purpose, which in turn influenced the development of new techniques and materials, and thus the overall aesthetic of model. Whether the process of abstraction is conscious or not, it creates room for the architects' and modelmakers' imagination to trigger, and better facilitates the explorative and communicative qualities of models.

In general, models made during the design process are more likely to be abstract, expressive and personal, in contrast to the models presented to clients or used at the end of the project. Abstraction allows the model to lose the restraints of accuracy in order to engage more freely with the creative process and so enables the architect to dismiss, if only for a short period, external pressures and focus on the formulation of concepts and ideas.

The selection of information and chosen levels of abstraction that enliven a model express the dynamism of the creative process. Indeed, during the process of creating study models, and to a degree presentation models, producers are more than simply reproducing a design, they are in fact designing a model that will translate and communicate a design. The making of the model is in itself a creative process. This is now a fairly recognised quality, similar to the craft of architectural drawings, and as such entitles models to have an artistic or conceptual identity of their own, distinctive to the information they represent.

With traditional modelmaking, a modelmaker maintains a close relationship with the architect, but is left to his/her own devices when concerning the fabrication of the model. The architect explains their vision and it is often up to the modelmaker to find a solution to its representation. And so the style of models and their creative process become the domain of the modelmaker. The architect's limited involvement with modelmaking occurs during the sketch model stage, when they are actually designing and creating space through the means of the model, but not necessarily designing a model as an object.

The model that is designed – no matter whether by the architect or the modelmaker – carries a great degree of credibility. One could argue that in architecture, the concept of craft is still highly regarded, despite all the digital work that flows through the contemporary practice environment. This fact goes some way to explain why 3D printing is still received with a lukewarm response by the architectural community. Its digital mechanisation is perceived as being outside the realm of creative craft, especially when compared to the handmade techniques of traditional modelmaking.

This chapter intended to contextualise the model within contemporary architectural practice and facilitate the investigation into the use of 3D printing for architectural models.

PART 2

3D PRINTING FOR ARCHITECTURAL DESIGN

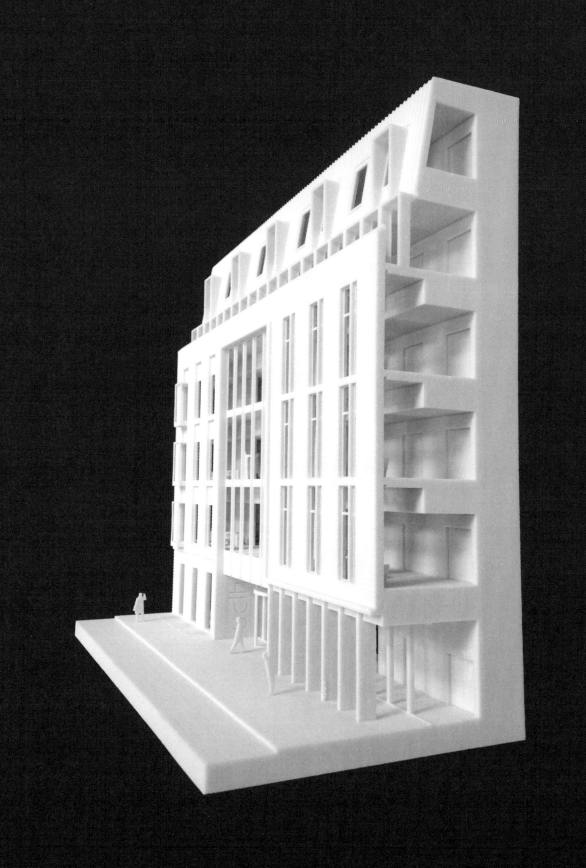

3D PRINTING FOR ARCHITECTURAL DESIGN

The use of architectural models in the 21st century has been drastically influenced by a material and technical revolution in the form of 3D printing. This technology has been particularly adopted for design models, resulting in a pronounced shift in both the aesthetic properties and working process of creating the model. Nevertheless, it has not yet become mainstream for modelmaking, nor has it wholly replaced traditional techniques of fabrication, but happily coexists with the numerous other mediums in use. In many ways, it is perceived as an addition to the catalogue of techniques available to represent architecture in three-dimensions. Yet, there has been very little substance in the examination of how its use affects the model as a tool for architectural representation. Most literature that can be found – often with nominal titles such as '3D printing for architecture' – specifically concentrate on the technical requirements for achieving a 3D print. If relatively little theory has been written on the model in general, even less has been done on the subject of the 3D printed model and its process of creation.

In the previous chapter, the model was explored as a process of craft and technique. What 3D printing has the potential to do is streamline this into a process of output. Even the use of the term 'printing' within the name '3D printing' creates the perception of a technology synonymous with two-dimensional printing; an association that alludes to a process not of creating a design, but of producing printouts. Making this connection can be both useful and problematic for architects. On one hand, there are instances such as internal reviews, where approaching a model simply as a printout of a CAD file may be acceptable. That the technology allows such a process is an advantage used by many. However, this use of 3D printing, where design is not an integral part of a model's creation, can be an issue if the model is to be utilised as an external tool for communicating specific information about a project. This is where a shift to approaching the 3D printed model as process of creativity, rather than output, can be advantageous.

Although commonly referred to as 3D printing, this designation has become somewhat of an umbrella term for a range of specific technologies based on material extrusion, sintering, lamination or liquid binding. Alternate terms that have come to generalise the technology also include rapid prototyping and additive manufacturing. The basic concept that applies to all forms of 3D printing is that it is an additive process in creating an object from a base material. Conversely, a prototyping technology such as CNC milling is a subtractive process, removing material to create an object.

The foundation for this range of technologies was the stereolithography format developed in the 1980s by Chuck Hull, founder of 3D Systems. From Hull's stereolithography (commonly known as SLA, a process of curing photo-reactive polymer with a UV laser), many variations of 3D printing technology have been developed and continue to be developed today. The most commercially used of these technologies include full-colour inkjet printing in a plaster material; selective laser sintering (SLS) in nylon; and fused deposition modelling (FDM) in thermoplastics such as PLA or ABS. In addition, other more advanced technologies and materials have also been created, being usually found in hi-tech industries and institutions. All these 3D printing variations have been applied in a range of different sectors, from medical sciences and aerospace engineering to fashion and consumer product design. And while 3D printing is increasingly being tested for finished products, it is still largely used for the purpose of creating prototypes and models of products-to-be.

The technology began to be utilised in architectural modelmaking in the second half of the 1990s. Some of the earliest adopters include Foster + Partners, Kohn Pedersen Fox Associates and Morphosis Architects. Architects were attracted by an increased accuracy of modelling, an exceptionally quick turnaround compared to other modelmaking techniques and the integration between the physical model and their growing digital platform of workflow. Although an expensive exercise when first introduced, 3D printing has now become a cost-effective alternative to some traditional models. Architects tend to use 3D printing to create whole models, which have little variation in material. Due to the nature of 3D printing, a completed model is typically a single solid object, regardless of how detailed or complex the geometry is. It is also very common for modelmakers to add a 3D printed medium into models fabricated from other materials, often altering the appearance of the 3D print part beyond recognition.

One of the most mainstream technologies for day-to-day modelling output in architecture is inkjet powder printing. This technology was developed by Z Corporation (now 3D Systems) and uses a white plaster compound material, layers of which are bound together with liquid binder. The final product may remain white through a clear binder application, or include full-coloured elements through the coloured binders used on certain printers. Inkjet powder printers can be a suitable technology for architectural practices to use as an in-house 3D printer, due to their output capacity, relative affordability and reasonable reliability. The models themselves are produced very quickly compared to other technologies of similar scale, and at an affordable cost. The fact that the models are produced in a neutral material in both looks and feel is also seen as advantageous for architects. The dullness of the material reacts to light far

better than the reflective surfaces and translucent materials of some other technologies.

It is important to note that architects and modelmakers do not solemnly make use of inkjet 3D printing, but also of various other technologies for their modelmaking, and in many instances to great effect. The specific technical characteristics of these fabrication processes, which are likely to dictate one's choice of use, constitute a wealth of information to comprehend. As the purpose of this research intends to consider the approach and use of techniques for digital modelling – regardless of 3D printing technology used – only a cursory understanding of an architect's options is required. An architect's use of Nylon SLS over inkjet powder for example, may be advised based on its ability to produce models with smaller tolerances, extra strength and of lighter weight. Compared to the inkjet technology however, it requires more lead-time for a model to be fabricated, can be a more expensive material, and does not support colour printing. Plastic technologies such as FDM are also being increasingly used by modelmakers to create add-on components for multi-medium models; nevertheless, it is not presently capable of creating entire one-piece models of a suitable size in a reasonable timeframe. Despite a number of other options available, architects, modelmakers and 3D printing bureaus have generally found the inkjet powder printing technology to most consistently meet their requirements for 3D printed design models.

The present use of 3D printing by the architectural industry – and in society in general – is much less sophisticated and not as widespread than it is portrayed in mainstream media. Excitement over the undeniable potential that lies within the technology to change our production methods has a tendency to sensationalise the technology to a point where laypeople have overinflated expectations of its present capabilities. This can particularly be the case within architecture, where its present use of modelmaking is underreported. Instead, attention is often given to speculative uses of 3D printing, purporting to change the way we construct buildings, such as in highly stylised and animated renders of 3D printed building concepts or full-scale habitable prototypes built in China. In reality though, this application of 3D printing is not yet practical and may never be a suitable alternative to traditional construction methods. Until these technologies are vastly developed beyond their current capabilities,

Below Visualisation showing how 3D printing technology can be used as a construction method. This steel pedestrian bridge, by MX3D and Joris Laarman Lab is planned to span one of Amsterdam's famous canals.

the most relevant use of the technology for architects is producing small-scale prototypes of their designs, i.e. models.

Looking at 3D printing exclusively from the context of modelmaking, it could also be argued that architects have underexplored the technology's present capabilities. While some of those that do use the technology to produce architectural models may perceive it as widespread within their industry, the amount of new architectural enquiries that approach professional bureaus indicates otherwise. Furthermore, as is the nature with early adoption of new technologies, initial use can be tentative and non-exploratory; newcomers have a tendency to simply aim to fulfil their requirement for producing a model, rather than immediately push the boundaries of what is possible to design a model. It is more natural for a new user to prioritise understanding the process of producing the object, before opening their minds to greater possibilities. And yet, in many cases, the greater possibilities or opening of minds never comes to fruition, and regardless of use, many architects continue to approach the technology as a form of output. Whether due to the human nature of sticking with convention or to a general lack of experimentation, it appears that many adopters of the technology do not move beyond the style of the simple models they managed to produce in the first place.

Aside from those who have adopted the technology, there are generally two groups of opinion regarding 3D printing for architectural models. First are those who view the technology's use as a cop-out for modelmaking. Their dismissal is not based on the technology being too easy (or complex for that matter) to use, but rather on the pretence that it is a method involving little skill or craft. They are preoccupied with the idea that 3D printing is limited to being a mode of output, and have likely not considered alternative approaches to creating models with the technology. The other common reaction to 3D printed models is one of astonishment. When architects present a 3D printed model to a client, the fact that it is 3D printed can initially be the dominant attraction, rather than the architectural concepts the model is trying to convey. Nick Dunn, Professor of Urban Design at Lancaster Institute for the Contemporary Arts at Lancaster University, believes there is also a lingering 'wow factor' with the architects themselves. 'We are still a little bit in awe of it at the moment. It still feels a bit space age, even though it has been around for a long time. Once we get past it people will start doing interesting things.'[11] Even for users not in awe of 3D printing, a better understanding of the potentials of the technology and the extent of what can be achieved will allow a more polished and perhaps respected output.

This section of the research will explain the nuances and changes that 3D printing has created with representing architecture in model form and explore the ability to approach the technology as an architectural craft.

2.1 THE 3D PRINTED ARCHITECTURAL MODEL

On the surface, it may appear that the use of 3D printing for architectural models is simply a development in modelmaking materials; powder, plastics and composites are perhaps only an alternative to wood, paper or card for producing the same device. The materiality of a 3D print is clearly unique, but has the technology in fact had a more profound effect on the architectural model? As with the established materials for modelmaking, 3D printing appears to have found its niche as a medium for design development models, particularly when examining its use as the primary medium of the object. As discussed in the previous chapter, study and process models used in the design process exist for the analysis and verification of ideas, and for communicating design intentions. By their very nature, these models are temporary in use, regardless of their material qualities or level of creative execution. They are not unduly valuable as an object, but are useful in achieving the outcome of the design process, and regardless of their quality of craft, can be considered as a form of output. The use of 3D printing to produce this type of model is therefore an instinctive occurrence, with its ability to produce a printout of a CAD file similar in manner to printing two-dimensional drawings for review. Used in this way, a 3D printed model also maintains a characteristic of expendability, and perhaps reinforces the recognition of the design model's transient nature, primarily due to the rapid production that the technology allows. This is evident in practices that regularly use 3D printing for modelmaking. For example, at PLP Architecture, Merryweather describes the practice's daily use of 3D printed models as 'just a pragmatic means to an end.'[12]

So in many regards, the essence of a design model is maintained when produced with 3D printing, despite a different appearance and materiality. The way that an architect is able to utilise a 3D printed model has however created new avenues of use, and an expanded functionality when compared to other more primitive mediums used for design models. Primarily, 3D printing has potentially broadened the areas that an architect can deploy the model during the design process. Traditionally crafted models pose enough of a laborious – and sometimes costly – endeavour that they are reserved for specific explorations or demonstrative requirements. Rather than limiting an architect to being overly selective with creating design models, 3D printing allows a greater range of three-dimensional representations to be produced in a given amount of time or budget. As more individual model typologies can be realised, an expansive yet more-specific range of information can be communicated or analysed physically. For example, an exploration of formal massing options can remain a study independent of content organisation or contextual considerations, before merging them all into yet another model within the design process.

Broadening the areas that an architect can use models is also based on what is perhaps 3D printing's greatest strength: it allows the communication of otherwise intangible digital information. Dunn notes that 'we can look at climate modelling, wear and tear, light studies and numerous other strategies that are sophisticated yet quite meaningless if you are talking to other people. It is not necessarily what a client, a member of the public, or a competition jury wants to see. So you can create these physical things being produced as totemic, they are kind of symbolic and a motif of the building. It is about taking all that information, which is quite divergent in a lot of ways – although it is quite holistic and connects to a project –

Below These models of the National Bank of Kuwait by Foster + Partners, use 3D printing to its full expressive capability. The three towers with colour applied use surface colour to illustrate environmental values, while the models in front employ actual geometry and colour to illustrate the values.

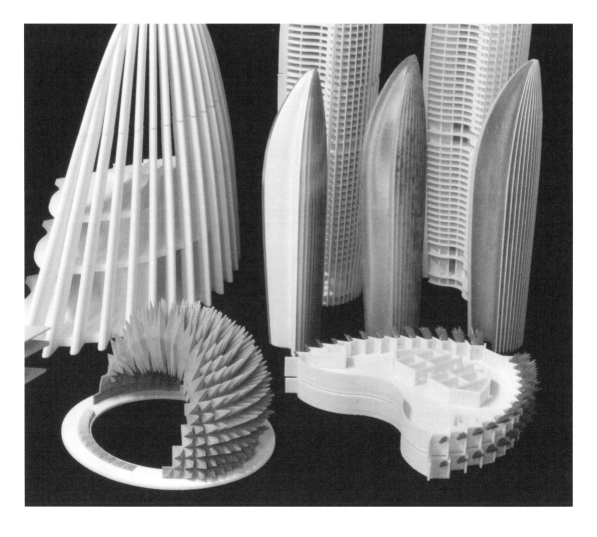

PROCESS MODELS
Design Model for Strata SE1, Hamiltons Architects

Above Displaying evidence of its use in the design process, the model has been freely drawn on. The value of this type of model is not neccessarily the object, but the discourse that it enables.

3D printing can be used to make design models of various types, and is particularly suitable for those primarily created as a tool for communication between design groups, engineers and contractors. Yui Law of Bogle Architects commissioned this model, while a part of Hamilton's, for their London project Strata SE1 in 2009. The model does not present any design options, and nor does it represent a design solution or resolved plan. Instead, it is strictly a process model that was used to instigate discussion and understanding towards the solution of a design problem.

The Strata SE1 features three wind turbines at its top. At the time this model was commissioned, the building was effectively designed and built up to the level where the turbines were to be installed. Despite this progress, there existed some ambiguities regarding the process of their installation, along with some related design details at the top of the tower. In order to better communicate with the various parties involved, Law created a model suited for the purpose. It resists being too suggestive of design intentions such as cladding, remaining open for solutions to be found; yet it conveys important specificities such as structure and concrete cores to guide accurate discussion between designers. According to Law, the use of colour to emphasise structure was important in aiding the communication between the structural engineers and himself.

Exemplifying a level of robustness, this model has travelled from various meeting rooms in London to Norway and Dubai, aiding the design of the turbines, extracts and building envelope, as well as to site where it was used to map the installation of brackets for cladding. It has been drawn on, added to and played with (it featured 3D printed spinning turbines) as a part of the design process, displaying how a working model can be achieved with 3D printing.

and actually creating something to be understood as an object that can be described and talked about.'[13] 3D printing can take a divergent set of information and through a process of digital convergence create a physical representation that can be used as a presentation tool.

If 3D printing can broaden the typologies of models, it also has the ability to produce numerous iterations of a single study. Moreover, the design process is affected by making it easier for an architect to translate their virtual models into physical representations for review. Dunn describes this advantage of 3D printing as creating 'a quicker feedback loop' over traditional models, which require a longer turn around. With 3D printing, 'you have already built the digital model, and you can actually print variations of that – different permutations – and look at them and inspect them. The processes by which you would go through in an over-all design development stage probably remain relatively unaffected, but I think the iterative loops are shorter and quicker. So you can probably move through that process faster.'[14] By creating more output in the design process, more information can be analysed and disseminated.

Above At 1:500, enough information can be shown on a project of this size to economically print many iterations of the design. Choosing a suitable scale for the context model at the beginning of the design process will yield most use throughout the project. Design evolution models for the Music Box by SPPARC Architecture.

Next Page 1:1000 masterplan/massing models consisting of a single context tile and many insert options. In addition to examining design solutions, these models can be used as communication tools to illustrate the narrative of a design presentation to stakeholders. Raglan Court models by Steffian Bradley Architects.

The ability to produce a greater number of models in a shorter period of time and within a specific budget also influences how an architect communicates with a client. Firstly, in-progress work becomes more accessible as more stages of the design process can be illustrated. Furthermore, the information is more readily understood, due to the approachable nature of models. Not only does this help a client better relate to their project, it also represents a better value compared to traditional models, according to Paul Treacy, Design Director at Steffian Bradley Architects in London. 'We produce a multitude of models now within the design process because they are more cost-effective, whereas previously we just produced one great model at the end. It is an easier sell for us to say "let's spend x amount on a 3D printed model" as a part of the process in order to get to a better end product. Rather than get to the end of the design process and then create a great looking model, for us it is about the process itself.'[15] Providing further value for the client, the quantity of models shown allows the merit of the design process to be conveyed.

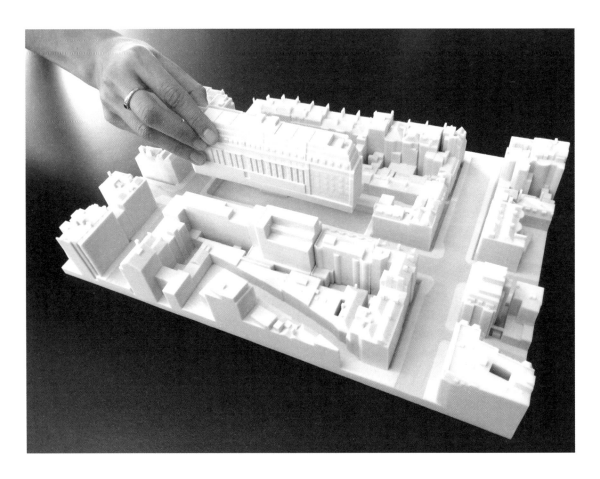

Above When designed to the correct tolerances, 3D printed models will fit together with precision. As shown with this model, this consistently repeatable trait can be advantageous when creating a number of inserts to compare differing design options. University College London Hospital, by Steffian Bradley Architects.

Left This model was used at a public consultation for the new Camden Town underground station. The 3D printed model suspended on acrylic rods is combined with an Ordinance Survey map printed on the base accurately projecting the location of entrances and underground infrastructure. Colour is also used to communicate various elements of this design proposal.

Another way 3D printing potentially changes the use of some design models is that it primarily becomes a tool for analysis and communication, rather than a physical medium for designing with. The object's materiality does not lend itself to being editable like a traditional sketch model, as its resolved composition has little relation to traditional processes of physically manipulating materials. Furthermore, the production accuracy of a 3D printer and nature of the technology's materiality results in an object that appears polished, without signs of human error such as glue marks, rough edges or ill-fitting elements. This appearance can potentially affect how the level of a project's design development is portrayed, implying a finalised design to a casual observer, when in fact the design it represents is still undergoing development. This issue can be particularly amplified if the model is prepared as a simple printout of digital information present in a CAD file. To combat this issue, an architect can control the amount of information that will be printed, through their use of digital modelling tools and intelligent techniques of abstraction. By approaching the model as a process of creation, the architect can avoid a model where the design may look over-resolved or finalised, which is particularly important when the purpose is communicating a select piece of information with others.

Beyond the fact that a 3D printed model's materiality differs from that of a traditionally crafted one, architects can exploit the technology to have a discernable effect on other physical details and qualities of appearance as well. Combining the capabilities of both a modelling software and a 3D printer, models can easily be coloured, texture mapped, incorporate any physical texture, include minute details and be tailored for printing at any scale.

Many of these qualities are an extension of the basic geometry being more accurate, since a model is composed of a single object rather than a sum of parts. This means each face of geometry will be exactly where it should be and should multiple models be required to fit together, tolerances can be designed into the objects that will allow a perfect fit. Advantages of the technology's accuracy also extend to the data set of a project as a whole. Models can be built at a particular scale and will precisely match a drawing printed at the same scale. This can also be advantageous in instances where digital information is projected onto the physical object. The NLA has taken advantage of this trait with their newly digitally produced London model, which according to Peter Murray, 'is so much more accurate than the previous hand built model, that we can actually outlay Ordinance Survey data just by taking it straight from OS drawings and we just project it on and it is millimetre accurate.'[16]

The use of colour in 3D printing can increase levels of realism and also create options for representing information that would otherwise be difficult to communicate in an object fabricated of a single material. Used

Below The New London Model was made by Pipers using a combination of hand craft, laser-cutting and 3D printing. Digtially sourced data creates a level of precision that allows themed projections to highlight urban characteristics with a high level of accuracy.

in a similar fashion to a multi-medium traditional model, colour has the ability to convey a range of architectural information and imply materiality. While machines with inkjet powder technology can print effectively any colour, many architects also make use of the range of greys that can be printed to emphasise spatial qualities or delineate specific information about a project. Aside from communicating architectural information, the use of colour is also an effective technique to imply a range of materiality in the object itself. As is common with traditionally crafted models, simply differentiating the base of model can have a desirable effect on the aesthetics of the object. Consisting of a single material, a stand-alone 3D printed model requires the use of colour if this or other material effects are desired. Again, the use of greys can be particularly useful in this manner, as they also retain a level of neutrality that is often desired by architects.

Despite the ability for 3D printing to easily create coloured models, colour remains a challenging feature to correctly translate on a model. According to Adam Nathaniel Furman, Director of Saturated Space, the root of this issue comes from the fact that 'colour looks totally different depending on the material in which it is contained, on the surface finish, and on the environment in which it is placed.' Similar to other modelling materials and techniques, 'a 3D printed model is a very rough and highly inaccurate simulation of colour, as it would be experienced from an architectural material.'[17] This issue of expressing accurate colour is perhaps exacerbated with 3D printing, due to some technical variables within the technology. First, there are hardware considerations that need to be understood – primarily print head alignment on an ink-jet 3D printer – in order for the printer to achieve consistent colour results. Furthermore, achieving a colour match for a desired colour can be difficult; the machine's ultimate output uses a CMYK process, whereas many digital modelling programs primarily handle colour in RGB, and the colour samples that architects attempt to match are likely to be in RAL or Pantone colour systems. To aid conversions between colour codes and the printed output, 3D printing bureaus and modelmakers can create a range of colour samples upon which accuracy tests can quickly be based upon. Despite the possibility of accurate colour, many architects shy away from its use. According to Merryweather, 'colour is so emotive and so risky to get right, it is just not practical' for regular use in practice.[18]

The difficulty of using colour in architectural models helps to introduce one of the more obvious and identifiable physical characteristics of a 3D printed model: literally how it looks. Whether it is the difficulty in matching colours or the architect's desire for neutral models, the 3D

Opposite This interactive model has the qualities of an illustration. Bold use of form and colour has been used to show the structure at a major regeneration area in West London, produced by Plowman Craven in Revit from laser scanning and other survey techniques.

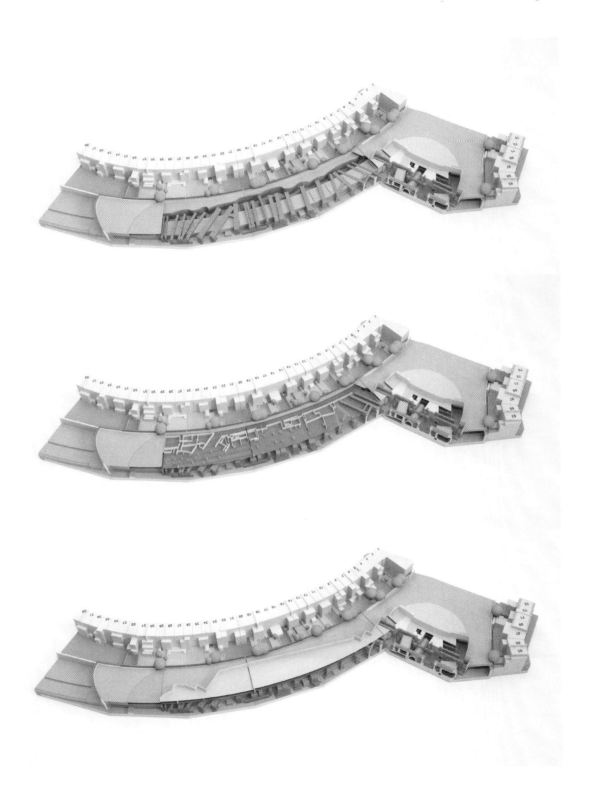

printed model has become well associated with the colour white. Further embellishing this neutrality is the fact that entire models are made out of a single material, compared to models crafted in more primitive materials, where an additional medium could visually separate a base or detail. These limitations of the technology are what form the requirement for computer modelling to be creative, maximising the visual purpose of the model.

Although this trend of monochrome 3D printed models may imply a lack of creative input to their style, it could be argued that architects have in fact converged upon a conventional aesthetic. Evidence of this can be seen in the way architects have drifted away from the full-colour model samples used to sell the technology to them in the first place. The vision of the Z Corporation engineers that created the full colour ink-jet 3D printing technology was one where the machines would be used to their fullest capabilities, producing colourful, realistic models. However, architects have long had a tendency to refrain from this kind of modelling, preferring a 'less is more' aesthetic. As Murray notes, 'totally realistic models have to be done very carefully otherwise they can look terribly naff and crude.'[19]

Above An example of the many full-colour models used by Z Corporation (now 3D Systems) to market their colour 3D printers to architects.

Opposite Above A selection of models at Steffian Bradley Architect's London office shows the reality of how most architects prefer to utilise the colour capabilites of inkjet 3D printing.

Opposite Below Even when placing a design within urban context or a landscaped environment, architects tend to maintain a monochrome aesthetic with their 3D printed models.

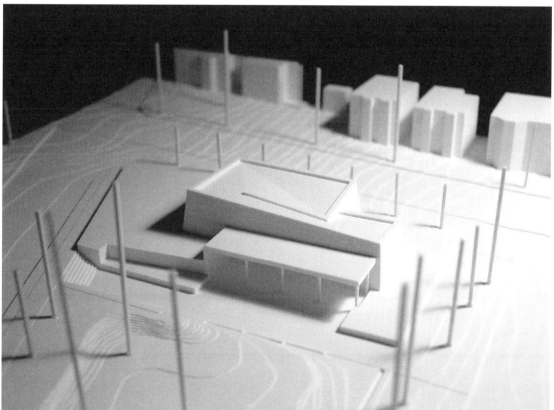

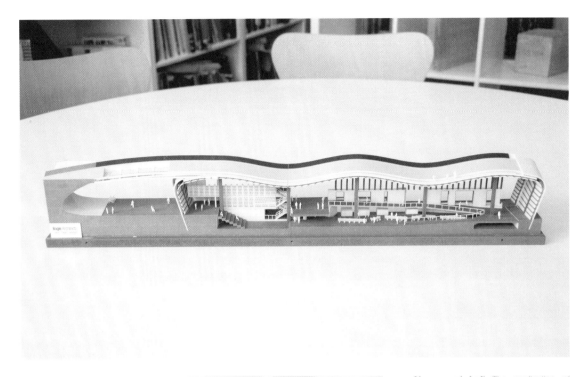

Above and Left The application of colour in this 3D printed model, while strictly a range of greys, effectively creates constrast between architectural surfaces and features, helping to communicate spatial qualities and enhance the quality of the design. Model for the Beijing Green Park proposal, by Bogle Architects.

This process of decolouring the 3D printed models points to the existance of common decision-making paths within architecture, some of which may arguably be unconscious. As architects have followed such trends to a point where many 3D printed models look similar, it would appear that there is now a common style established. It is almost as if, when someone says 'I would like a 3D printed model,' they are referring to a style of model, rather than a model in a particular medium. But in draining the models of colour, architects seem only to have followed convention, rather than consciously produce a style of note.

Perhaps the most significant characteristic of 3D printing that has influenced a de-stylised aesthetic is the lack of physical craft involved in the design of the object. As the produced model is an exact reproduction – literally a printout – of digital information in an architect's CAD files, the situation exists where the model is essentially an output of information, rather than a creation of an object. With a massing model made in wood or another traditional material, the architect, modelmaker or designer is also reproducing information, but does so in a completely different medium to what the information is copied from. This could be digital information translated into the physical medium, but it occurs through the modelmaker's craft. Within that translation, certain physical decisions can be made which influence the style of the model: the type of material, joins, textures, detailing, etc., can all provide evidence of authorship. Despite its physical and tactile qualities, the 3D print – and particularly its craft – should be considered a digital medium, where its quality as an object is dependent on the design quality of the digital information used to create it.

One of the risks of not approaching the design of a 3D print in this manner is that when exported simply as a reproduction of CAD data, the object may hold less value than the file itself. Reflecting the present state of 3D printing for architectural models, Dunn states that 'at present, there is not much value in the object as an object in itself. The value is in the model and of course it is a digital model. The physical model is just a simulacrum. Once you 3D print something, you can chuck it, because you have got the file.'[20] Conversely, a highly crafted model will be valued for its craft as an object. To better appreciate a 3D printed model as an object, its source of creativity needs to be the digital file prepared for printing. This can range from carefully designed and abstracted features to finding ways to express valuable content that already exits within the virtual model. For example, Steffian Bradley Architects sometimes use 3D printing as a tool for translating the value of their Building Information Model (BIM) to the client, increasing the usefulness of the physical ob-

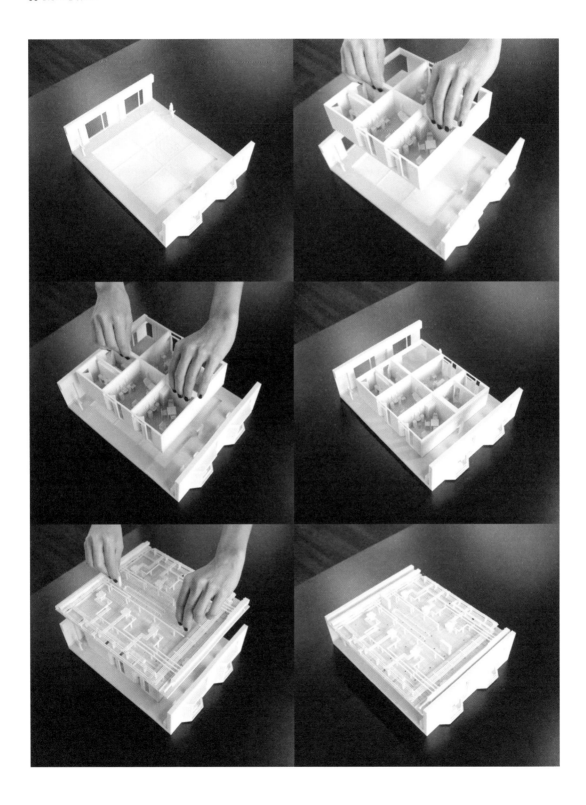

ject. Architects that regularly use the technology as a means for producing development models, and particularly those that exploit the digital file as a medium for design do, in fact, perceive the model as a valuable object.

In summary, a 3D printed architectural model has the potential to be a medium to be of greater interest if a digital process of craftsmanship is undertaken. As the end product possesses physical properties, there exists a platform for tangible stylisation. Some architects may fall into the assumption that because the model is digitally produced, it is easy to do and it therefore ends up being bland. This lack of translation can be overcome by approaching the model as a creative process rather than a process of output. By understanding the translation of digital craft into a physical object, 3D printed models can be better appreciated by their creators, users and audiences.

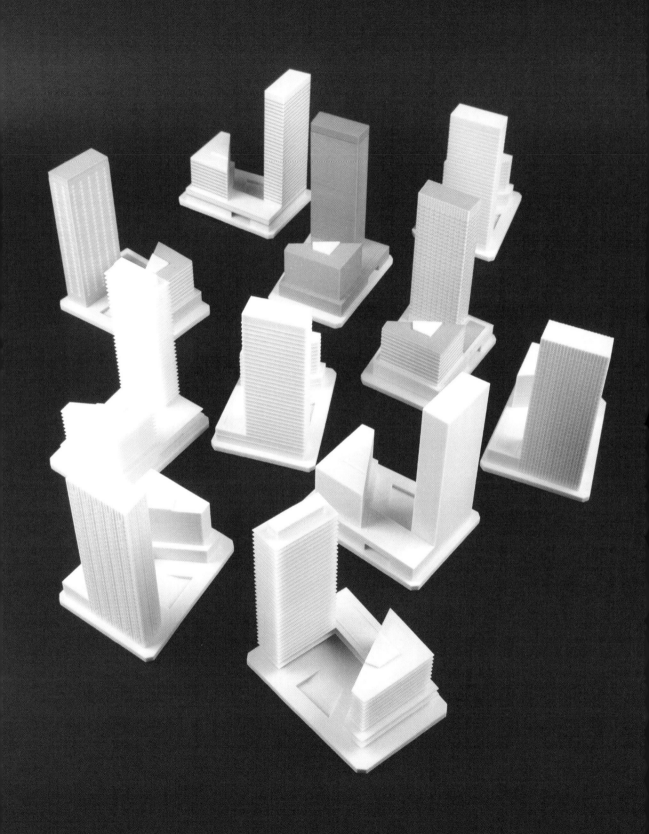

2.2 THE DIGITAL MODELMAKING PROCESS

Having established that the 3D printed model is a physical medium born out of a digital process, the methods of creating the model can be looked at in more detail, including the relationships and responsibilities involved in its production. The creation of architectural representation through a digital process is not a groundbreaking concept. Drawings, diagrams, renders and other visualisations are now predominantly achieved through the click of a mouse. However, of all the visual tools available to an architect, 3D printing is arguably the primary medium that actually allows a physical illustration of digital content. Translated into the medium of a model, the comprehension of this digital information is transformed; formal qualities are better understood through the eye's perception of space compared to a viewport or an image printed on paper. To maximise the effectiveness of this translation and ensure a successful model, it is important to understand the nuances of the 3D printing process.

Whether a model is intended to be a simple printout of information or a highly stylised design exploration, digital modelling for 3D printing requires adherence to some basic geometric principles. Drawing with this understanding enables the final preparation of data for printing to be more easily accomplished by 3D printing specialists. However, exploring these technical requirements is not the purpose of this research and there are numerous technical sources on these concepts that architects and modelmakers can refer to. Alternatively, this research requires the understanding of how and when to deploy extracurricular techniques for improving 3D printed models. For example, if a model is to be used as a simple printout of a digital model for internal purposes, following the basic guidelines for 3D printing may be all that is required to produce a successful model. However, if the model is being used externally or to communicate a specific idea or set of information to its audience, an architect may be inclined to stylise the model. In this case, a designer should not only be mindful of the basic data requirements for 3D printing, but also – and more importantly – emphasise their approach to designing the model as an object. To maximise this design potential, understanding the techniques achievable through 3D printing technology will ultimately provide a more usable and accomplished 3D printed model.

Regardless of their desired model use and the resultant approach to modelling, it is unrealistic to expect architects to consistently provide ready-to-print data to 3D printing specialists due to the constant state of flux of a design file. The fluid nature of the design process also means that

Opposite The style of a 3D printed model can vary depending on the application of a range of digital modelmaking techniques.

revisions will inevitably occur up to the point of being sent off to print, further compromising the ability to produce perfect data. This is where a modelmaker with 3D printing expertise, and particularly a professional 3D printing bureau can provide invaluable assistance in the delivery of a model. Describing Steffian Bradley Architects' use of their 3D printing service, Treacy says, 'We send it to them, get them to evaluate it, give us a cost quotation, and they can print the model almost instantly. If they see a significant glitch in the model, they will come back and say, "Guys are you sure about this?" So there is always a backstop.'[21] Based on the ability of a 3D printing service to polish the provided data, sensible digital modelling should be all that is required to produce a high quality model.

The use of any specific 3D modelling program to design the model should not be of concern to a designer either. 'The process of translating data is so easy now. Ten years ago there was a complexity about it, you had to send the right kind of file, and it had to be tested or validated, and I think because at that time it was perceived as an expensive undertaking, you had to get it right and use the correct program,' says Treacy.[22] For 3D printing, easy to use programs such as SketchUp are just as capable as more complex ones, such as Rhino, MicroStation or AutoDesk Revit. Any variation in the quality of the exported data will be particularly insignificant if the digital model has been formulated with the basic requirements for 3D printing.

Rather than concern oneself with the program of use, it is therefore more important to focus on designing the digital model as a physical architectural model. This sounds an obvious recommendation, but many architects simply export their digital information as it is and rely heavily on the 3D printing specialist to translate this into a print-ready state. However, this process does not necessarily guarantee that the digital model will be optimised for 3D printing. On the other hand, if the architect designs the geometry to correspond appropriately to the intended scale and respects the limitations of the 3D printing technology being used, there is more potential for the model to be produced as intended by the architect. Furthermore, the architect must ensure that they supply a finished design for their model and not rely on additional input from the 3D printing specialist. While the latter may be capable of editing digital objects, they are not in fact providing a design service and thus will not add flair or style to the model. In this instance, the resulting 3D print is simply an output of a drawing file, which as explored previously, may be an appropriate solution for some uses. In contrast, by taking the drawing file aside and preparing it as an object, the designer can begin to apply techniques that will activate it beyond a three-dimensional export of a

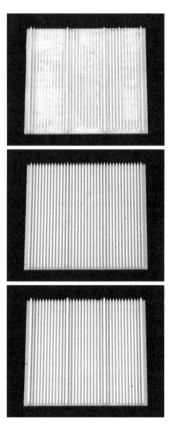

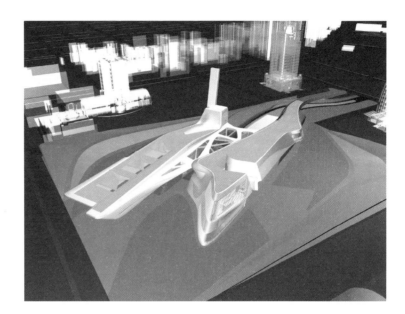

Right and Below The translation from digital data (right) to physical model (below) has become a very streamlined process for those architects who regularly make use of 3D printing.

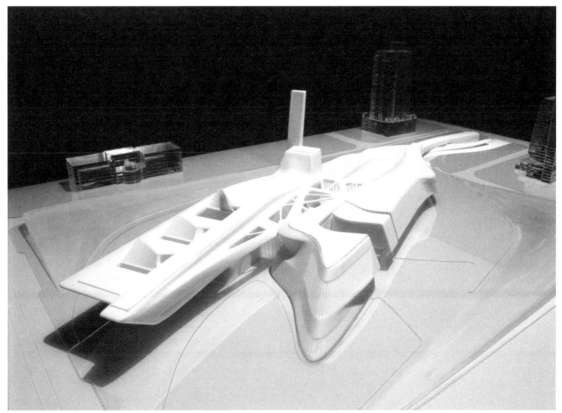

CONTEXT MODELS
Urban Context Model Data Sourcing

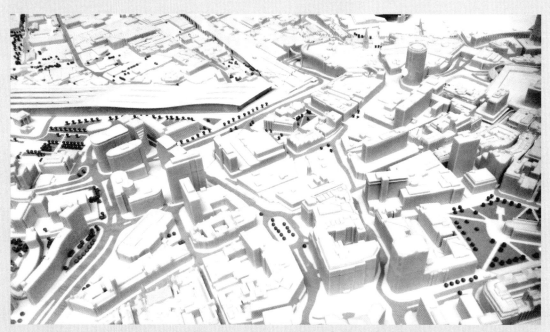

3D printed context models increasingly rely on the use of detailed 3D data sets of the urban environment. Architects source this data from specialists in the creation of accurate digital models of cities, using aerial imagery, 3D scanning, photogrammetry and 3D modelling to construct these digital models. The use of such data provides architects with accurate modelling of a site's local context and environment. Employing three-dimensional surveys is also increasing in importance due to its integration with Building Information Modelling (BIM).

At present, there are companies that offer their data at various levels of detail. This can range from Level 1, where buildings are effectively featureless masses modelled to an accuracy of 100cm, to Level 4, where buildings and their architectural features are modelled to an accuracy of a few centimetres.

There is a discernable cost difference between the various levels of urban data, which obviously correspond to their respective levels of detail.

As the use of this urban data becomes more prevalent, it is possible that the future style of 3D printed context models could be affected by new techniques in data collection. Presently, the data for lower levels of detail are primarily gathered from above, often creating detailed roof information on a context model that otherwise indicates only formal massing. As 3D data gathering technologies become more advanced, a higher level of detail could be achieved in the more basic packages of digital urban models. Should this be the case, architects looking to 3D print their context models may be able to achieve a high level of accuracy or, in other cases, wrestle with this level of detail in finding the right balance of abstraction.

Above and Opposite Model of central Birmingham, UK, used at a 2015 public consultation on the proposed Curzon Street station.

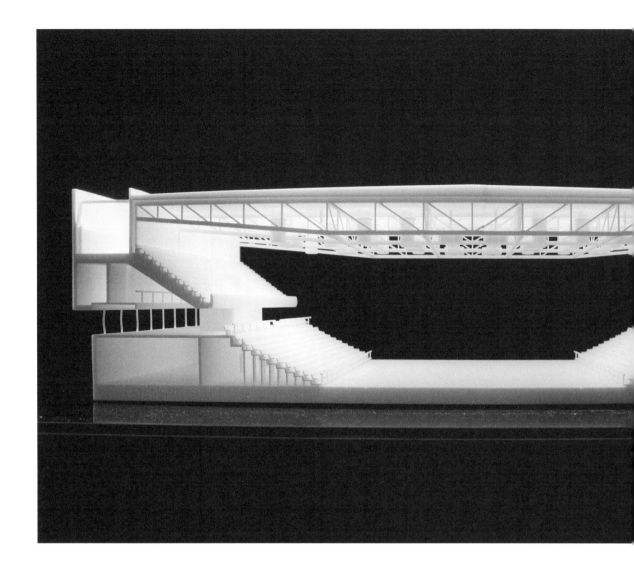

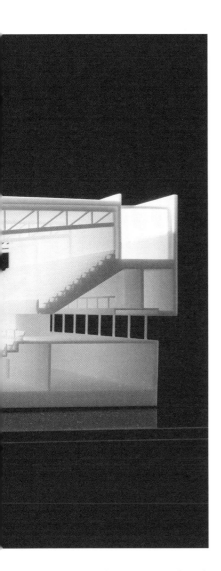

CAD file. The difference in the end product between a model of 'output' and one that has been creatively detailed is apparent. This potential is not dependant on the modelling program of origin, as it only requires a change in the designer's mental approach.

To further emphasise this concept, it is valuable to have a deeper understanding of the general workflow for producing a 3D printed model. There are unquestionable differences between the fabrication techniques used in 3D printing with those of traditionally crafted models – operating a machine is vastly different to a scalpel. There are also distinctions with the process of planning, designing and sourcing a 3D printed model. Although these nuances have a profound impact on how a model is conceived, they are perhaps less consciously acknowledged by those engaged in the process of creating it.

Most models are first brought to life in the same manner: an architect encounters the opportunity or requirement for a model and engages the process of creating one. The type of model, scale, subject matter and desired effects are all considered at this stage. The methods of creating either a 3D printed or a traditionally crafted model diverge soon thereafter. In the latter's case, the architect may provide a modelmaker with a brief and relevant drawings. Through this discourse, the modelmaker is able to recommend specific materials and techniques that will best exhibit the qualities of the project that the architect is trying to convey. The production of the model is then dependent on how the modelmaker utilises their skills and the tools at their disposal. To a considerable degree, the resulting style will be influenced by their aesthetic decisions and technical abilities. In this path of workflow, many of the details of the model are the domain of the modelmaker.

The use of 3D printing to produce an architectural model reworks this process. Firstly, the main point of contact for the architect is likely to be a 3D printing service; specialists in data preparation, operating 3D printers and post-print processes of model preparation. Modelmakers are not always displaced within this approach, particularly if a practice has their own in-house group. In this instance, the modelmaker can act as an intermediary between the architect and 3D printing service, or even as full-on operator of a machine should a practice have one. In fact, the technical ability to operate 3D printers is increasingly becoming an additional capability of a modelmaker's skillset.

Where the mediums and tools used to produce a traditional model are manipulated solely by a modelmaker, the devices used to produce a 3D print are split between the architect and a 3D printing specialist. The former uses a computer program to create a drawing file and the latter uses a 3D printer to produce the physical model from that data. All properties of the end product are dependent on the combination of how well both of these tools are employed. The design quality of the model will be a direct result of the architect's use of digital techniques, while the finishing quality is influenced by the craft of the operator.

While the tools used to produce a model are now the domain of both the architect and the specialist running the 3D printer, the techniques of stylising the model are now entirely the architect's responsibility. The architect no longer provides a modelmaker with a drawing set and concept for the purpose of guiding the craft of a model. They are providing three-dimensional drawing files, which contain precisely what will be reproduced by the digital manufacturing process. The opportunity is therefore present for architects to establish their own craft of modelmaking – albeit a digital one – and create a personal style with 3D printing. In doing so, they can begin to control the language of their 3D printed models in the same manner as they do other mediums of representation, establishing a coherent style and continuity of expression in their work.

As previously discussed, this requires a change in the mental approach to the process of creating a model, from one of output to one of actually designing the model as an object. However, there is a notion that CAD is not an appropriate platform for design to take place. Exploring the inherent difficulty of designing on a computer, Dunn explains, 'that when you draw a line with a pen or a pencil as an architect, you are thinking about that mark on the paper. You are thinking about what that is, what sort of thickness it has, what sort of texture it has, etc., even though it might just be a rudimentary demarcation of space or material on a sheet. But when you build something in CAD, you do not necessarily think about what these lines mean; what you're actually thinking about is the precision of how they join. You're not thinking about design decisions. The whole thing is predicated on a need for modelling precision, without all the richness of thought about what those things are. So I think this is one of the reasons that so many 3D prints look the same. You can kind of skip a step when you are building a digital model in 3D, because it is influenced very heavily by accuracy.'[23]

By consciously recognising the need to combine the requirements of modelling accuracy in CAD with the quality of thought to affect the nature of those lines, Dunn agrees that it is possible to 'stylise the single-print object. I think it's an emergent area of research and I have not seen it done particularly well yet.'[24] Indeed, those that are making the effort to craft their digital model files, such as Treacy, admit that to 'translate personality into the model, it takes time to develop these techniques,

Opposite 3D printed models alongside a traditionally made architectural model, illustrating the different levels of information that can be communicated by each respective technique. 1:500 models by PLP Architecture.

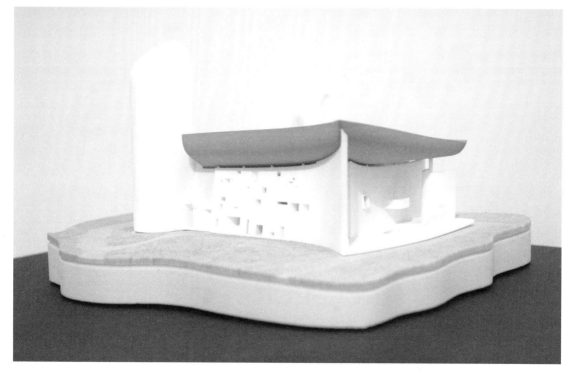

Opposite Model of the chapel of Notre Dame du Haut by Le Corbusier, produced by Digits2Widgets. The model was created through an extensive undertaking of digital modelling, based on original drawings and hundreds of photographs to acheive an accurate representation of Le Corbusier's masterpeice in Ronchamp. By creating a digital file with physical textures, appropriate detail sizes, colour, interior elements and a removable roof, this model exemplifies how stylistic techniques can improve the qualities of the object itself.

before it becomes a matter of course.'[25] In many ways, an architect with a developed body of techniques for digital craft will be able to proficiently execute their model design in a similar manner to how modelmakers rely on a number of shorthand techniques to efficiently construct a traditional model.

The realisation of this working method of digital craft is key for the architect to unlock the potential of their 3D printed models. Jonathan Rowley, Design Director at Digits2Widgets notes in an interview that, 'So many people still have their minds so blown with the fact that 3D printers will make them a shape that they are not actually paying very much attention to how much you can also influence the surface texture. All of the joy and brilliance of 3D printing is in the CAD file. The printer is just a machine that whoever is designing needs to understand and then when you have married those two together, you can get something pretty special.'[26] To a greater extent than the machines used to print it, the 3D printed model is limited by the technology used to design it, and this technology is only limited by the imagination of the people that are using it.

CONCLUSION

This research has shown that to a great extent, the successful execution of a 3D printed model is the responsibility of its designer. But what does this understanding afford and what are the potential advantages of improving the style of 3D printed models? In order to approach these questions, one can consider the reasons why an architect stylises their other modes of representation. Time is spent on drawings, renderings, diagrams and traditional models, tweaking them to ensure they convey exactly what the architect intends. In contrast, it is odd that many architects have fallen into the habit of simply exporting their data to produce a 3D printed model, regardless of its intended use. Because this methodology has become commonplace, many models end up looking similar and ubiquitous. Applying a digital process of craft allows a 3D print to be more unique.

This individuality can be achieved by considering a CAD program and its functions as a tool of craft. In the previous chapter, it was noted how similar tools used by different people can create vastly different styles, which is also true of 3D printing. Treacy reinforces this idea when stating 'I could give one person a piece of data from our Revit model, give them a brief saying this is what I want, and I am pretty sure that in other people's hands I would not get the same product every time. It comes back to the idea of being able to craft a stylised approach to actually communicate the design information in a successful way. I think there is a skill there that is inherently not tangible in the product.'[27] Approaching the process in this way, 3D printed models can be better integrated with a practice's house style of representation.

It is important to highlight the lack of publication and promotional use of images of 3D printed models compared to their traditional counterparts. While an image of any model inherently loses the value of the physical object, the ability to use photographs of a more sophisticated 3D printed model will at least provide a practice with additional material, which would otherwise be discarded. Improved design consideration will enable architects and audiences to better appreciate the model, increasing its value as a design and communication tool.

Finally, by applying a process of digital craft to the model, the ultimate advantage will be a more capable model for communicating an architect's ideas. As the 3D printed model is most associated with the design process, the ability for it to convey an architect's intentions is of high importance. According to Karen Moon in Modelling Messages, 'only when the model is engaged as a creative tool of expression is it fully utilised, becoming, like two-dimensional sketching, an intrinsic part of the architect's thinking about the design.'[28]

PART 3

TECHNIQUES FOR STYLISING
3D PRINTED ARCHITECTURAL MODELS

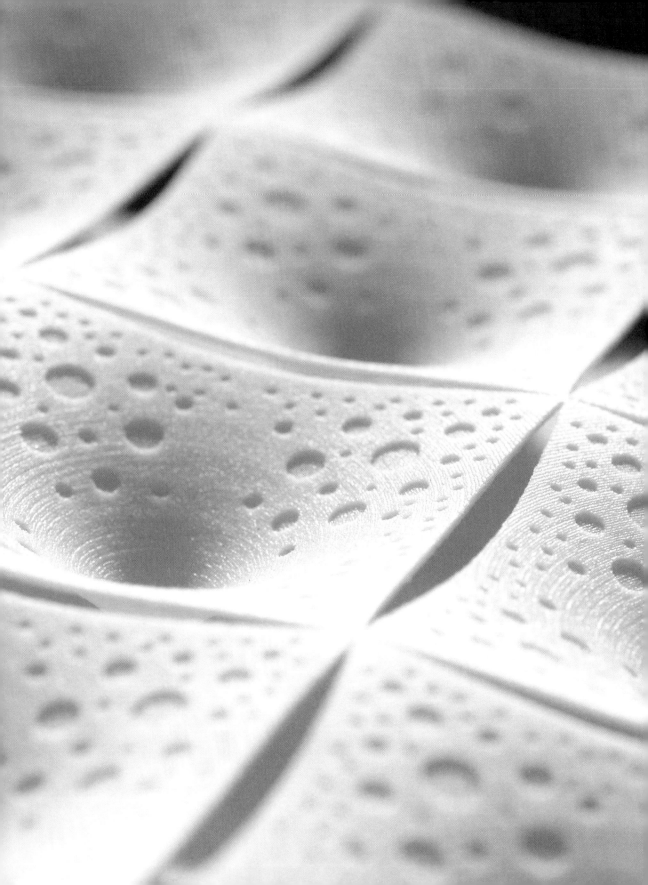

TECHNIQUES FOR STYLISING
3D PRINTED ARCHITECTURAL MODELS

The final part of this research explores various stylistic techniques that can be used in the digital modelling process in order to create more interesting 3D printed architectural models. The examples shown reflect particular types of models where modelling techniques can enhance the style or communicative abilities of the object. It is important to note that many of these techniques are not specific to determined purposes and their concept of style can effectively be applied to various model typologies. For example, physical textures are used to exemplify the application of that modelling technique, rather than the specific application of 3-dimensional materials, such as brick. This section includes explorations such as specific abstractions of geometry; the use of physical textures, colour and texture mapping; and the ability to animate models with 3D printed narrative.

The techniques highlighted on the following pages can be achieved in effectively any 3D modelling program. Furthermore, they also represent fairly basic stylistic manipulations, which do not consume a great deal of time to incorporate into one's digital preparation for 3D printing. If used regularly within the process of data preparation, many of these techniques have the potential to become a shorthand method of representation, at which point they can be built upon further by a designer's creative instincts.

Recalling what was outlined in the second part of this research, it is important to have an understanding of the capabilities of the specific 3D printing technology being used. While most techniques can be achieved with any type of 3D printing, some technologies may achieve better results than others, or require a different sensitivity to tolerances or minimum sizes.

Although the techniques in this part may predominantly be highlighted in isolation, this has been done primarily for the purpose of clarity. The application of a combination of techniques can often be used to great effect on a 3D printed architectural model. It is also useful to note that the example models shown have not been combined with any other model-making mediums, emphasising the digital technique at hand.

As an architect's palette of digital representation tools is effectively limitless, the techniques set out in this part are by no means exhaustive. Rather, they represent some of the more basic techniques that one can utilise, and when combined with the understanding of the overall process, they can provide a platform for further explorations of the 3D printed model's stylistic potential.

Opposite 3D printed roof model showing the use of physical textures, which have been modelled digitally and optimised to suit the 3D printing technology in use.

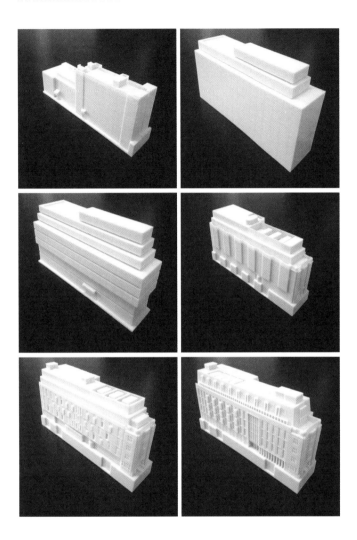

Levels of Abstraction Perhaps the most common technique utilised when preparing a file for 3D printing is simply the abstraction of architectural geometry. This may relate to the level of information that the particular model may require or as a supplemental technique for the aesthetics of the model. Abstracting geometry may be more commonly done at an early stage in the design, when certain details may not be resolved enough to be included in models used for other analytical purposes, such as massing. As shown by this set of models which were used in the development of the same project, the levels of detail and abstraction can vary depending on the stages of design.

Levels of Abstraction As designs become further developed, a more thorough exercise of editing geometry may be required to achieve the desired representation. This can be for a number of reasons relating to the object's aesthetics, but is also importantly linked to its physical properties being suitable for the 3D printing technology in use. As with other modelmaking mediums, the abstraction of façade elements is particularly appropriate with smaller scale models, such as the tower shown.

Abstracting Architectural Forms 3D printing is very effective in representing numerous types of information on solid architectural forms (patterns, ornament, etc.) but there is a difficulty in representing transparency – i.e., glass. This means that 3D printing often ends up limiting glass-intensive projects to being massing models. This need not always be the case. Modelling the floor plates while maintaining elements of the buildings form can be an effective way to communicate transparency.

Floor Plates and Massing Models When creating massing models of many different design iterations, a commonly used convention is to represent floor plates which can give a sense of scale to a form where little ornament or detail exists at this stage in the design. Methods for achieving this are effectively unlimited with 3D printing. Floor plates can be indicated through a range of geometric manipulations and through the use of colour (top left).

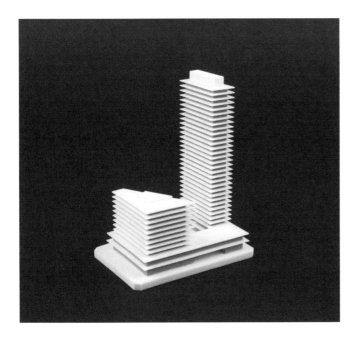

Diagramming Information Here, the use of colour to indicate building use combined with the floor plates gives an example of how information can be layered within a single model. A model such as this can be used to direct a discourse about the form and use of the building without addressing the façade.

Complex Geometry As complex architectural geometry has its base of existence in CAD, 3D printing is the perfect medium for expressing such forms. While much of the model's style may be a result of the architectural design itself, the specific optimisation of the geometry as a scaled object can help clearly define the various forms and their relationships.

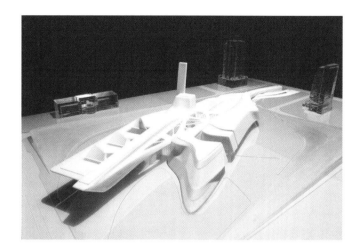

Simplified Geometry Achieving a simplified aesthetic with 3D printed design models can be achieved by 'editing down' the amount of information in the CAD file. Contours, while crude, can deliver more information about the typography than a complex mesh.

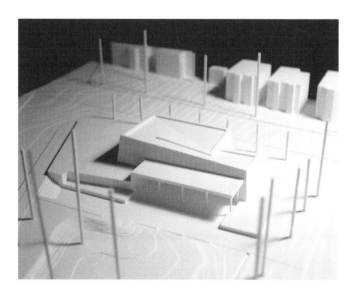

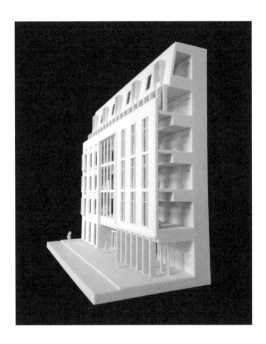

Vertical Section Models The section drawing is an essential tool for understanding a design. 3D printing is well suited to making section models. Once a model has been designed, cuts can be taken as required prior to printing. The example shows a façade study and the section reveals its relationship to the interior. Another use of the section model might be to split a building in two so that the model has two purposes - as a complete model and as a sectional model.

Horizontal Section Models Horizontal sections can be prepared in a similar manner to their vertical counterparts to be used as part of a series of floors or as a stand-alone object. Typically, sections are taken just below the ceiling to reveal the interior space.

Insert Models The context model with proposed building insert is a standard convention of architectural modelmaking. The treatment of how the insert relates to the context will affect how the model is used. In the example shown, the proposed building fits into a recess in the context tile. This has the advantage of keeping the prososed design correctly positioned. Recessed inserts can also be used to reveal basement levels. Often, the insert defines the site boundary which affords greatest flexibility as the design develops.

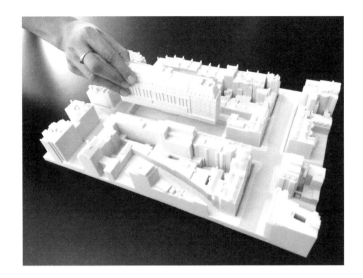

Assembled Models 3D printing allows the designer to easily create a model in sections. In the image shown, the lift away part is designed to show the horizontal section of a typical apartment. This technique can also be useful for creating a kit of parts where a scheme is broken down into constituent parts of varying sizes and forms allowing a hands-on design workshop at an early stage in the design process.

Abstraction of Materiality As a design progresses. there will be much detail in an architect's CAD file. Once envisioned at the model's scale, this information is often too extensive or small to be either crafted or 3D printed. The designer preparing the digital model is required to extract the precise information they desire and do so in a manner that compliments both the intentions of the architectural project and the aesthetic of the model itself. As exemplified by this model, this will often require an understanding of minimum thicknesses or gap sizes to create an effective representation of materiality.

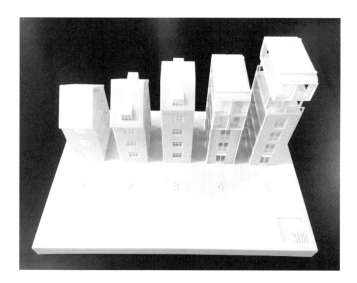

Text 3D printing can be used to activate an architectural model's communication abilities through the utilisation of modelled text. This can be used for actual architectural features such as signage, be diagrammatic in nature, or simply be used as a tool for labelling models with a practice's branding, model title or model scale.

Physical Textures Utilising physical textures are an effective technique when applied to 3D printed models. The amount of textures available is limited only by the imagination of those creating the digital model. Physical textures can be particularly useful with monochrome 3D printed models to add a level of detail or differentiation of architectural information that might otherwise be difficult to achieve in a single material model.

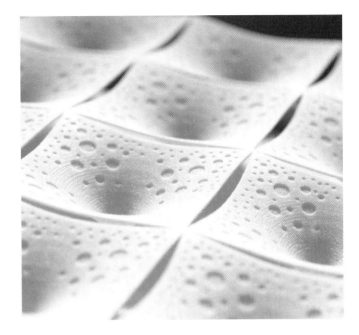

Material Thickness Intelligently representing the transparency, translucency or opaqueness of architectural forms can go a long way to create an aesthetically pleasing architectural model. While traditional modelmaking can achieve these things through the use of different materials, 3D printing in a single material creates the requirement for creative thinking about how to represent these things.

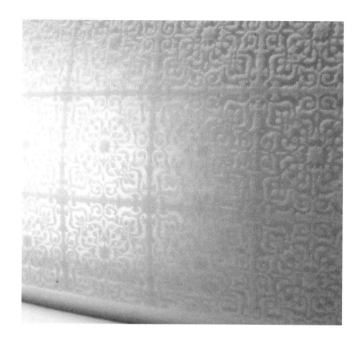

Physical Textures Creating a physical texture for 3D printing can either be modelled from scratch, or obtained through the use of design tools or plug-ins, which extrapolate 2-dimensional data and quickly create 3-dimensional forms. For the best results, the designer must ensure that they understand the scale of the model and the true sizes that the texture heights will be, once printed.

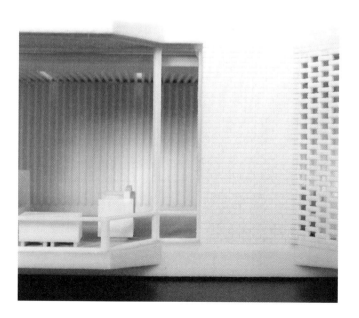

Physical Textures Material qualities, such as brick, in this example, can be effectively modelled with physical textures. Using this technique to represent materiality is both clear and subtle, not overpowering the overall model.

Physical Textures Abstracted material representation can be an effective way to imply a design idea regarding materiality, even at an early stage of design. Rather than relying on the existence of precise architectural data, creating a textured surface can easily expand the role of a design model.

Physical Textures All kinds of materiality can be represented or subtly suggested by the application of physical textures.

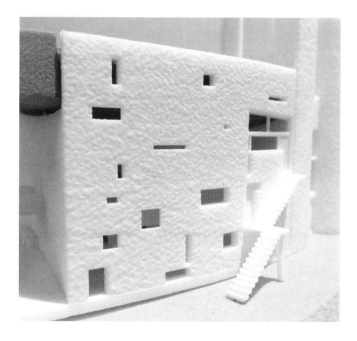

Colour Colour can be an effective way to communicate many things in a model, such as programme use in massing models, indications of materiality, or creating definition between various elements of a model. With inkjet powder 3D printing technology, the application of colour is not only possible but also reasonably easy to achieve. There are various ways that colour can be applied to the digital model and will be slightly different depending on the software in use. Once the colour information is attached to the data, it is important to export a file format that will carry that colour information.

As explained earlier in this research, the colour matching and output process can take some experimentation to gain exact matches. If colour accuracy is of utmost importance, experimentation with small swatch samples or access to a system of 3D printed references is the best way to achieve precisely matched colours.

Colour and Massing Models A common use of colour is to indicate areas of building programme on massing models or even imply zoning in an urban scale masterplan. Using colour in this manner is a simple way to help clarify narrative and aid communication at an early stage of design. Applying colour to a digital model for this purpose can be quickly achieved and can be matched to the output of any respective drawings or diagrams that might also indicate the same information. Such attention to detail will only serve to bring clarity to the communication of design intentions.

Colour and Massing Models The use of colour is an effective technique of representation for early design models.

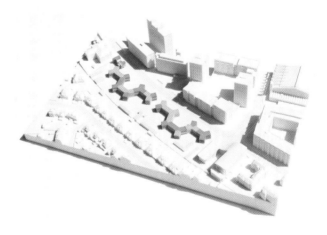

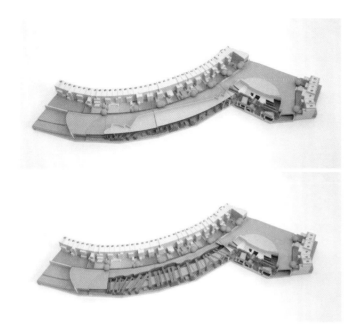

Colour and Materiality Colour can be applied to a model to imply materiality and help create a hierarchy of information. In this model, the stylised use of colour combined with its sectional qualities, allows the model to perform in a diagrammatic fashion indicating various elements such as context, levels, structure and use.

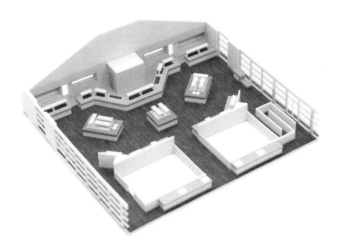

Colour and Materiality This 1:100 colour model of a servery uses flat colours applied to the surfaces and an image texture applied to the floor. The timber flooring is clearly visible and this limited use of texturing adds expression to the model.

Colour and Materiality As design development advances, colour can be used to effectively represent materiality. Similar to analysing formal massing options, 3D printing allows multiple options to be quickly materialised.

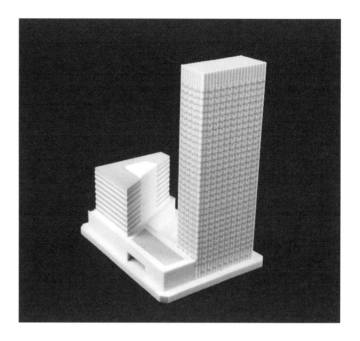

Colour and Materiality Using flat colour to represent materiality, rather than using a texture-mapped image of an actual material (see page 100) can maintain an element of abstraction within the model. Depending on the effect or representation desired, it may be that the elements carrying the colour in the model will need to be compartmentalised in order to show a larger variation of colour on a single surface.

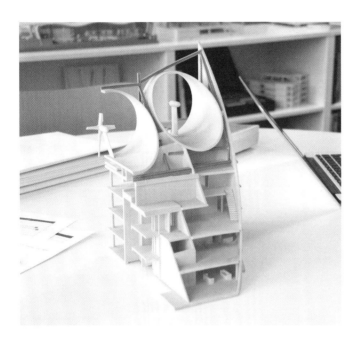

Colour and Materiality Colour has been subtly used on this model to highlight certain structural elements, aiding and directing design conversations between architects and engineers.

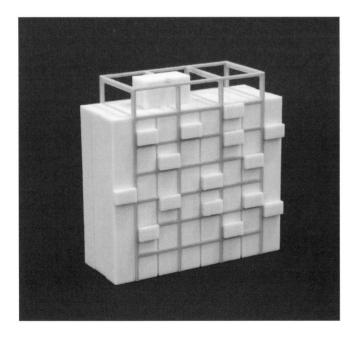

Colour and Materiality In the image shown the orange frame demands attention while the white massing recedes and takes a contextual role. Use of jarring bright colour can prevent the model from appearing to be a fixed design.

Editing Colour Once a digital model file is prepared to handle colour, many variations can be easily achieved.

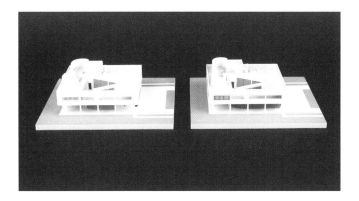

Creating Contrast with Colour Colour can also be used to add definition and visually separate elements of a model. Used in an intelligent and subtle manner, this can have a similar effect as combining mediums in modelmaking; for example a good use of this technique would be to create a patterned or textured surface. These models show how combining colour and geometry can subtly vary the emphasis of a pattern.

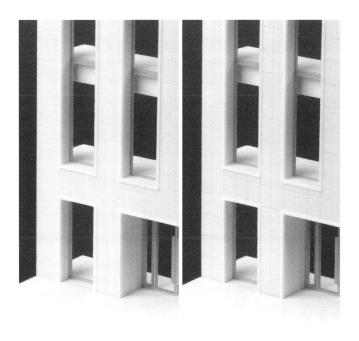

Mapping Technical Information Colour can be utilised with 3D printing to create physical representations of engineering or technical survey data such as wind and solar analysis or structural loading. This information can be sourced from analysis software, which can typically create a texture map applied to the digital model. Models such as these, produced by Foster + Partners, can be an effective way to communicate technical information.

Combining Mediums This model not only uses colour to indicate different zones of an underground station, but is also combined with a printed base, showing how the infrastructure relates to its surroundings.

Creating Contrast with Colour One of the more effective ways to use colour in 3D printing is to create contrast between even the simplest of elements. In this model, colour has only been used to indicate roads, trees and green spaces, creating a much more visually engaging object than if it had been left completely white.

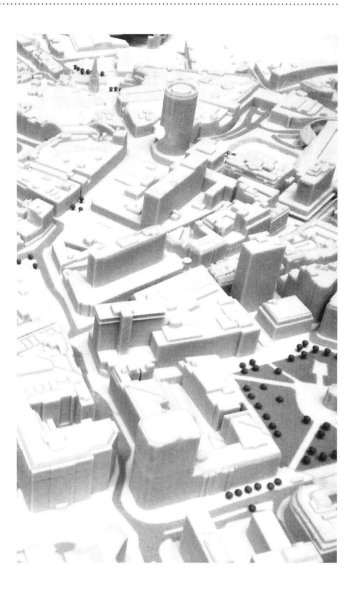

Creating Contrast with Colour The application of grey is perhaps one of the most effective uses of colour in 3D printing. Used smartly, it can enhance the visual qualities of a model greatly while maintaining a level of neutrality so often desired. It can also be particularly effective in creating a visual separation for the base of a model, as shown here.

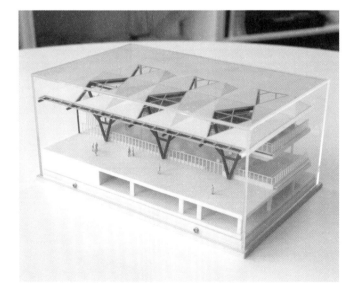

Creating Contrast with Colour Grey is particularly useful when creating a hierarchy of the information at hand, similar to how an architect might manage a drawing or diagram.

Creating Contrast with Colour This model makes use of colour to accurately represent the materiality of Le Corbusier's Notre Dame du Haut. In limiting the colour palette to subtle tones and few elements, the model manages to maintain a neutral aesthetic.

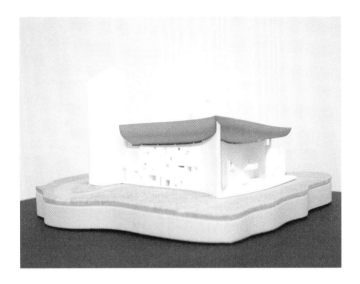

Creating Contrast with Colour Using colour when representing interiors can be beneficial for communicating with clients, suppliers and interior designers. It can be beneficial for indicating mood, atmosphere and the intended design language of architectural space.

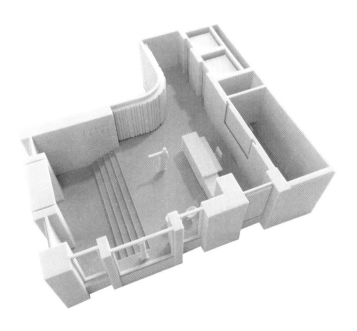

Texture Mapping In instances where a degree of realistic representation is desirable, texture mapping is a technique that can be used to translate this information onto a physical model. This model has had a brick render material applied in CAD and exported for 3D printing. Texture mapping can also be used in abstract manners, as the essence of the process is effectively mapping any image onto a digital surface. It is important to note that success in texture mapping is often determined by scale and characteristics of the material applied. Colours in textures that are printed too small can become muddy and unfocussed. The image shown printed at 1:100 is the smallest scale that bricks can be distinguished.

Editing Texture Maps In order to achieve a desirable result, the colours in the source file may require some manipulation. If the texture map is jpeg based, this can be achieved in Photoshop, whereas a material file can usually be edited within the CAD program. These models have all had the same source file applied, with only the material's colour balance, brightness and saturation manipulated to create this range of colour options.

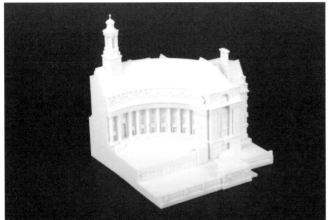

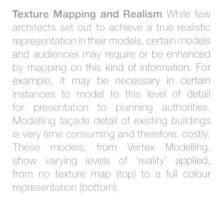

Texture Mapping and Realism While few architects set out to achieve a true realistic representation in their models, certain models and audiences may require or be enhanced by mapping on this kind of information. For example, it may be necessary in certain instances to model to this level of detail for presentation to planning authorities. Modelling façade detail of existing buildings is very time consuming and therefore, costly. These models, from Vertex Modelling, show varying levels of 'reality' applied, from no texture map (top) to a full colour representation (bottom).

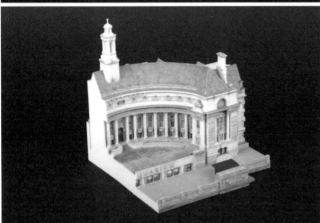

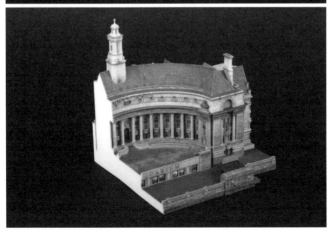

Texture Mapping Context Information
Texture mapping can be used to convey
context and is also an effective technique
for showing environmental information in site
and topographic models.

Animating a Model Constructed in any
medium, a model will always perform better
with elements of narrative and life. The ability
to digitally model and print these elements
makes this easy to achieve with 3D printing.

Animating a Model Creating a story or narrative increases a model's power of communication. This can be achieved with 3D printing, either by designing and printing accessories as individual parts and attaching them afterwards or by including them on the printed object.

Also note the effective use of text, colour and abstracted architectural forms (in this case an interior wall), which combine to create an engaging model.

Animating a Model Although there may be a temptation to simply export CAD information as it is in the source file, editing and abstracting this information becomes particularly important with interior models. This model shows how taking the time to design various elements of a model can create a beautiful object and ultimately aid the communication of architectural information.

Animating a Model It can be useful to digitally model furniture and interior furnishings for the purpose of showing not only scale, but also giving the ability to communicate a better understanding of space for the layperson.

Animating a Model One of the best ways to activate a model with narrative is by populating it with activities, people, events, and other objects that take up space in our environments. The manner in which these are applied to a 3D printed model will depend on the scale, style of elements and technology used to print the model.

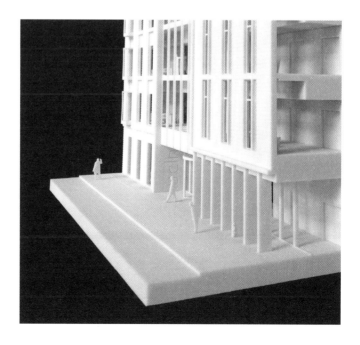

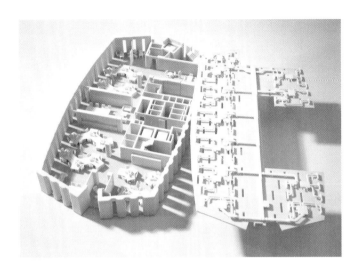

Building Services The close relationship between a 3D printed model and its digital source of geometry means that effectively any available CAD data can be represented physically. As shown in this model, building services extracted from BIM (Building Information Model) allow this type of information to be visualised in model form. For this to be successful, it is important to adapt this geometry for the purpose of becoming a scale model.

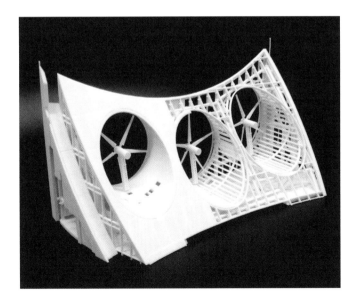

Structure and Cladding Intelligent editing of the abundance of information available in a CAD file can lead to highly interesting models. In this example, the designer has balanced the amount of cladding to remain on the model with the amount of structure to be exposed.

Structure 3D printing allows structural concepts to be quickly translated from digital to physical model.

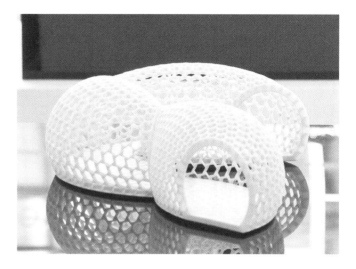

Structure Physical models can help to aid design discussion and communication of a range of architectural information.

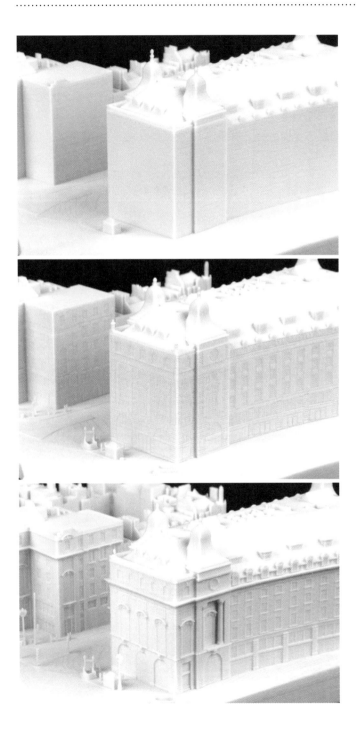

Urban Data Urban data with varying levels of detail can be purchased from various sources. The time and cost of digitally modelling façades of context buildings can mean that only adjacent buildings carry a higher level of detail, as can be seen on the model on page 33. It is sometimes said that complexity is free with 3D printing. While this might be the case for the cost of the actual printing, it is not the usually the case for the digital modelling.

The 3D printed models shown are all derived from a digital model created by Vertex Modelling. Although there are automated data gathering techniques, to obtain a model of professional standard usable for 3D printing, some level of manual modelling is required. Vertex Modelling have modelled most of central London and are constantly maintaining the model as the city develops. Many cities around the world have digital city models that are usable to a greater or lesser extent for 3D printing.

Mapping Drawings and Diagrams A more abstract example of using texture mapping, this model shows the possibilities of representing effectively anything that originates from an image file, which can be mapped onto a surface in CAD. This could be sourced from photography, or even a sketch or hand drawing that is projected onto a surface. On a more resolved project, more complex line drawings such as elevations could also be projected to give an interesting effect. This could possibly assist with context models, where details may be needed to help identify surrounding buildings but there is either not enough time to model them, or a need to save the expense of sourcing 3D scanned data.

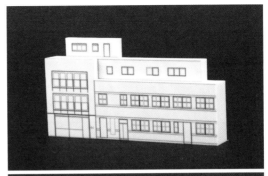

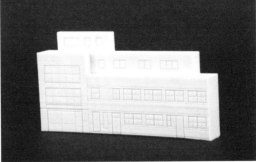

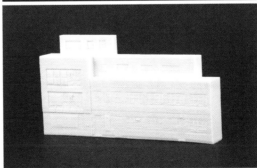

NOTES

1   'Drawing Out Meaning', *RIBA* [website], (n.d.) < http://www.architecture.com/
    Explore/Stories/DrawingOutMeaning.aspx >, accessed 17 Jul. 2015.
2   Nick Dunn, *Architectural Modelmaking* (2nd edn., London: Laurence King
    Publishing Ltd, 2014), 14. For an intereseting and concise description of the
    model's history, see 'A Brief History', chapter in *Architectural Modelmaking*.
3   Karen Moon, *Modelling Messages: The Architect and the Model* (New York: The
    Monacelli Press, 2005), 33.
4   *Ibid*, 47. See for a more extensive exploration of the architectural model's
    vulnerability, 47-9.
5   *Ibid*, 91-92.
6   *Ibid*, 84-5.
7   Peter Murray, interview with the author, 2 Sep. 2015.
8   *Ibid*.
9   Neil Merryweather, interview with the author, 17 Aug. 2015.
10 Michael Graves, 'Thought Models', in Suzanne Buttolph, *Great Models:
    Digressions on the Architectural Model* (Raleigh, NC: North Carolina State
    University, 1978), 43.
11 Nick Dunn, interview with the author, 27 Aug. 2015.
12 Merryweather, interview with the author, 17 Aug. 2015.
13 Dunn, interview with the author, 27 Aug. 2015.
14 *Ibid*.
15 Paul Treacy, interview with the author, 4 Sep. 2015.
16 Murray, interview with the author, 2 Sep. 2015.
17 Adam Nathaniel Furman, correspondence with the author, 7 Sep. 2015.
18 Merryweather, interview with the author, 17 Aug. 2015.
19 Murray, interview with the author, 2 Sep. 2015.
20 Dunn, interview with the author, 27 Aug. 2015.
21 Treacy, interview with the author, 4 Sep. 2015.
22 *Ibid*.
23 Dunn, interview with the author, 27 Aug. 2015.
24 *Ibid*.
25 Treacy, interview with the author, 4 Sep. 2015.
26 Quote taken from interview with Jonathan Rowly. Laura Griffiths, 'Le Corbusier
    Remastered', TCT Magazine, Aug. 2015, 57-9.
27 Treacy, interview with the author, 4 Sep. 2015.
28 Moon, *Modelling Messages: The Architect and the Model*, 80-1.

FURTHER READING

Bertram, Peter (ed.), *The Makings of an Architectural Model* (Copenhagen: The Royal Danish Academy of Fine Arts, School of Architecture Publishers, 2012).

Buttolph, Suzanne, *Great Models: Digressions on the Architectural Model* (Raleigh, NC: North Carolina State University, 1978).

Driscoll, Matthew, *Model Making for Architects* (Ramsbury, UK: Crowood, 2013).

Dunn, Nick, *Architectural Modelmaking* (2nd edn., London: Laurence King Publishing Ltd, 2014).

Griffiths, Laura, 'Le Corbusier Remastered', *TCT Magazine*, Aug. 2015, 57-9.

Karssen, Arjan & Otte, Bernard, *Model Making: Conceive, Create and Convince* (2nd edn., Amsterdam: Frame Publishers, 2014).

Martens, Bob, Mark, Earl and Cheng, Nancy Yen-wen, 'Thresholds between Analog and Digital Representations', *Communicating Space(s)* [24th eCAADe Conference Proceedings], Volos (Greece) 6-9 Sep. 2006, 372-83.

Moon, Karen, *Modelling Messages: The Architect and the Model* (New York: The Monacelli Press, 2005).

Morris, Mark, *Models: Architecture and the Miniature* (Chichester, UK: Wiley-Academy, 2006).

Sheil, Bob (ed.), *Manufacturing the Bespoke: Making and Prototyping Architecture*, AD Reader (Chichester, UK: John Wiley & Sons Ltd., 2012).

Smith, Albert C, *Architectural Model as Machine* (Amsterdam: Elsevier, 2004).

Stavrić, Milena & Šidanin, Predrag & Tepavčević, Bojan, *Architectural Scale Models in the Digital Age: Design, Representation and Manufacturing* (New York: Springer-Verlag/Wien, 2013).

Stevens, James & Nelson, Ralph, *Digital Vernacular: Architectural Principles, Tools, and Processes* (London: Routledge, 2015).

Werner, Megan, *Model Making* (New York: Princeton Architectural Press, 2011).

Holtrop, Anne, Teerds, Hans & Floris, Job (eds.), *Models Maquettes*, OASE Journal for Architcecture 84, (Rotterdam: NAi Publishers, 2011).

ONLINE RESOURCES

Astbury, Jon, 'Architects do it with Models: The History of Architecture in 16 Models', *The Architectural Review* [website], (25 Feb. 2014) < http://www.architectural-review.com/view/architects-do-it-with-models-the-history-of-architecture-in-16-models/8658964.article>, accessed 16 Jul. 2015.

Doscher, Martin, 'Morphosis Prints Models', *Architecture Week*, (18 Aug. 2004) < http://www.architectureweek.com/2004/0818/tools_1-1.html >, accessed 17 Sep. 2015.

'Drawing Out Meaning', *RIBA* [website], (n.d.) < http://www.architecture.com/Explore/Stories/DrawingOutMeaning.aspx >, accessed 17 Jul. 2015.

'Modelmaking in the Digital Age Symposium Videos', *B.15 Modelmaking Workshop (Univeristy of Manchester)* [blog], (13 Jan. - 2 Sep. 2015) < http://blogging2.humanities.manchester.ac.uk/sedlab/?tag=modelmaking-in-the-digital-age >, accessed 15 Dec. 2015.

Olcayto, Rory, 'Architects Must Embrace 3D Printing', *Architects Journal* [webiste], (15 May 2013) < http://www.architectsjournal.co.uk/comment/architects-must-embrace-3d-printing/8647975.article >, accessed 28 Sep. 2015.

Pohl, Ethel Baraona, 'From Line to Hyperreality', *Domus* [website], (12 Mar. 2012) < http://www.domusweb.it/en/architecture/2012/03/12/from-line-to-hyperreality.html >, accessed 15 Dec. 2015.

IMAGE CREDITS

Front Cover © SPPARC Architecture, 3D printed context model for the Music Box.

1 © SPPARC Architecture **14** © John Donat/RIBA Collections **16** © RIBA Collections **17** © Patrice Meigneux/Corbis **18** © RIBA Collections **20** Taken by the author **21** © Lasdun Archive/RIBA Collections **23** (top) © Feilden Clegg Bradley Studios **23** (bottom) © Henning Larsen Architects **24** © Agnese Sanvito **25** (all) © KREOD **27** (all) © Ryan Kingsnorth **28** © Agnese Sanvito **30** © Scales & Models **33** © RIBA Collections **38** © Steffian Bradley Architects/Andrew Putler **41** Taken by © Lee 3D, Make Architects **42** © Joris Laarman for MX3D **44** © Steffian Bradley Architects/Andrew Putler **46** © Nigel Young/Foster + Partners **47** (all) Taken by © Lee 3D, courtesy of Bogle Architects **48-49** (all) © SPPARC Architecture **50-51** (all) © Steffian Bradley Architects/Andrew Putler **52** (top) © Steffian Bradley Architects/Andrew Putler **52** (bottom) Taken by the author **53** (all) © Agnese Sanvito **55** Taken by © Lee 3D courtesy of Plowman Craven **56** © Lee 3D **57** (top) © Steffian Bradley Architects/Andrew Putler **57** (bottom) Taken by the author **58** (all) Taken by © Lee 3D courtesy of Bogle Architects **60** © Steffian Bradley Architects/Andrew Putler **62** © Lee 3D **64** © Lee 3D **65** (all) © Zaha Hadid Architects **66-67** © Edwin Ellis Creative Media **68-69** © Make Architects **71** Taken by © Lee 3D, courtesy of PLP Architecture **72** Taken by the author, courtesy of Digits2Widgets **78** © Lee 3D **80** © Steffian Bradley Architects/Andrew Putler **81** (top) © Lee 3D **81** (bottom) Taken by © Lee 3D, courtesy of PLP Architecture **82** (all) © Lee 3D **83** (top) © Zaha Hadid Architects **83** (bottom) Taken by the author **84** (top) © Steffian Bradley Architects/Andrew Putler **84** (bottom) © fabriek.org by Tiemen Schotsaert **85** (top) © Steffian Bradley Architects/Andrew Putler **85** (bottom) © fabriek.org by Tiemen Schotsaert **86** (all) © Steffian Bradley Architects/Andrew Putler **87** (all) © Lee 3D **88** (top) © Lee 3D **88** (bottom) © Steffian Bradley Architects/Andrew Putler **89** (top) Taken by the author **89** (bottom) Taken by the author, courtesy of Digits2Widgets **90** © Lee 3D **91** (top) © Lee 3D **91** (bottom) © Steffian Bradley Architects/Andrew Putler **92** (top) Taken by © Lee 3D courtesy of Plowman Craven **92** (bottom) © Lee 3D, courtesy of Benchmark Designs **93** (all) © Lee 3D **94** (top) Taken by © Lee 3D courtesy of Bogle Architects **94** (bottom) © Lee 3D **95** (all) © Lee 3D **96** (top) © Nigel Young/Foster + Partners **96** (bottom) Taken by the author **97** © Edwin Ellis Creative Media **98** (all) Taken by © Lee 3D courtesy of Bogle Architects **99** (top) Taken by the author, courtesy of Digits2Widgets **99** (bottom) © Steffian Bradley Architects/Andrew Putler **100-103** (all) © Lee 3D **104-105** (all) © Steffian Bradley Architects/Andrew Putler **106** (top) © Steffian Bradley Architects/Andrew Putler **106** (bottom) © Taken by © Lee 3D courtesy of Bogle Architects **107** (top) © KREOD **107** (bottom) Creative Tools AB [Flickr] under license CC BY 2.0 **108-109** (all) © Lee 3D